Geomedical Aspects in
Present and Future Research

Geomedical Aspects in
Present and Future Research
Symposium

Arranged by

The Norwegian Academy of Science and Letters

in collaboration with

The Academies of Sciences of Denmark, Finland, Iceland
and Sweden

and sponsored by

The Nordic Culture Fund

and

The Norwegian Cancer Society

Organizing Committee
Gunnar Gissel Nielsen, Denmark
Joakim Donner, Finland
Ólafur Bjarnason, Iceland
Olav Gjærevoll, Norway
Jon Jonsen, Norway
Jul Låg, Norway
Olav Sandvik, Norway
Arne Semb-Johansson, Norway
Allan Danielsson, Sweden
Frans E. Wickman, Sweden

Conference Chairman
J. Låg, Norway

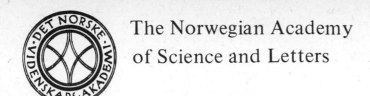

The Norwegian Academy
of Science and Letters

Geomedical Aspects in Present and Future Research

Editor: J. Låg.

Universitetsforlaget

Oslo – Bergen – Tromsø

© Det Norske Videnskaps-Akademi 1980
ISBN 82—00—12654—4

Universitetsforlaget
Distribution offices:

NORWAY
Universitetsforlaget
Box 2977 Tøyen
Oslo 6

UNITED KINGDOM
Global Book Resources Ltd.
109 Great Russel Street
London WC 1B 3ND

UNITED STATES and CANADA
Columbia University Press
136 South Broadway
Irvington-on-Hudson
New York 10533

Printed with contribution from:
Norges landbruksvitenskapelige forskningsråd
(The Agricultural Research Council of Norway), Oslo

Printed in Norway by
Hammerstads boktrykkeri, Oslo

Preface

The question of setting up a wider geomedical research project in connection with the international programme Man and the Biosphere (MAB) was taken up in Norway in 1971. But development of the idea has been a slow process. It was not until 1977 and 1978 that the Norwegian Research Council for Science and the Humanities and The Agricultural Research Council of Norway made funds available for two projects that originated from the discussions of the Norwegian MAB-committee.

The Norwegian Academy of Science and Letters suggested to its fellow Nordic academies that a geomedical symposium should be held as one of a series of cross-subject internordic symposia. When this was agreed to the following committee was elected:

Dr. Gunnar Gissel Nielsen, Denmark
Professor Joakim Donner, Finland
Professor Ólafur Bjarnason, Iceland
Professor Olav Gjærevoll, Norway
Professor Jon Jonsen, Norway
Professor Jul Låg, Norway
Professor Olav Sandvik, Norway
Professor Arne Semb-Johansson, Norway
Dr. Allan Danielsson, Sweden
Professor Frans E. Wickman, Sweden.

Professor Låg was chairman.

The Norwegian Academy of Science and Letters has received economic support for the organizing of the symposium from The Nordic Culture Fund (Nordisk Kulturfond) and from The Norwegian Cancer Society. The Nordic Culture Fund gave a grant of 50.000 Danish Crowns, and The Norwegian Cancer Society

(Landsforeningen mot kreft) covered the travel and hotel expenses of a lecturer from USA. The Academy whishes to express its thanks for this valuable help.

The Symposium was held at the Academy, Drammensveien 78, Oslo, on May 22–23,1978. Since this was an internordic symposium, most of the lectures were given in the Scandinavian languages. Posters also played a role in the arrangements. Both the lecturers and the poster-exhibitors were requested to deliver a comprehensive English summary and a complete list of references for publication.

One important reason for the Symposium was to provide a reciprocal orientation for, and contact between, researchers engaged in the various fields of geomedicine. With this in mind the arranging committee, in its choice of contributors, tried to cover as many as possible of the important fields with the subject. Not all of the lecturers we hoped to have were able to attend, and since some lecturers could not be present for both days of the symposium the arrangements had to be altered to suit their schedule, and this way vary from the sequence given in this publication.

Some of the discussions that followed the lectures were delivered in written form afterwards, but the material was so heterogeneous that it has not been possible to include it in this volume.

The Editor has tried to produce as uniform a publication as possible but the papers contributed varying as they do in form and length, have modified this. We hope that the material presented here will, however, be of interest to other researchers besides those who took part in the Symposium, and that the material may form a basis for continued research activity in this extensive and difficult field.

The Symposium ended with a general debate. Many of those present voiced the hope that the internordic geomedicinal co-operation initiated by the Symposium would be continued. It is possible that scientists in other countries will, at a later stage, be interested in joining an organized research effort.

It must be emphasized that geomedicine is a very wide and

complicated field, and that a successful solving of the problems necessitates the inclusion of researchers involved in widely differing specialities. Future geomedicinal symposia may well have to be limited to specific facets of the total complex of subjects involved.

The Symposium arranged was carried out in coordination with the Academies of Sciences of the Nordic countries, and it was agreed to appeal to these institutions for help in countinuing the promotion of geomedical research.

Contents

10

Survey of Geomedical Problems, Including Some Examples from Investigations Carried out in Norway

J. Låg

For quite a long time the importance of the part played by environmental factors in the geographical distribution of diseases of human beings has been recognized. A study of the history of science will show that Hippocrates and a few other Greek writers dealt with such problems 2400 years ago (see e.g. Jacobi 1930, Henschen 1962). However, these dissertations from antiquity did not have any important influence on the further development of the subject.

In recent times, knowledge concerning so-called endemic diseases, i.e. certain diseases with a characteristic geographical distribution, has gradually emerged. Further investigations showed that environmental factors influenced several of these diseases. A classical example is the elucidation in the last half of the nine-teenth centry of the relationship between goitre and lack of iodine. Further examples may be mentioned, such as the detection of the relationships between dwarfism and lack of zinc, and bet-ween caries and lack of fluorine.

The term geomedicine has been given various meanings by different authors. It is difficult to formulate a good definition of the subject. However, geomedicine may be defined as the science dealing with the ordinary environmental factors influencing the geographical distribution of pathological and nutritional problems relating to human and animal health. The effect of the so-called interior environmental conditions should not be included. The influence of the environment in assembly and working rooms should thus fall outside the subject of geomedicine, as should genetically based problems. Subdivision of this comprehensive subject is desirable.

The proposed definition differs to some extent from previous explanations. Some authors have considered geomedicine and geographical medicine as synonyms. Often veterinary medicine has not been taken into account in defining this subject. Instead of the term geographical medicine, on several occasions, the expression medical geography has been used.

As far as can be ascertained, the term geomedicine was introduced by Zeiss (1931). Both Zeiss and Rimpau (1934) stated that geomedicine ought to be considered as an independent science, and that research workers with quite different skills should participate in solving the problems.

A rough systematization of the subject may be based on the classification of environmental factors. The climate has a direct influence on geomedical problems. Important questions are related to soil conditions, and on this basis a large group of problems could be distinguished. As is known, the climate influences the soil and will thus have an indirect effect in addition to the direct. Influence on vegetation is a very important part of the effect of the soil condition. The term edafo-geomedicine is a designation proposed for this group (Låg 1972). When the geomedical problems are connected to the water supply, the expression hydro-geomedicine may be used. During discussions on Norwegian geomedical investigations, chemical influences of the climat will be mentioned.

Some scientists have included plant diseases in geomedicine (cf. the term geophytomedicine). However, this science falls outside the definition used here, but correlations can be found between plant diseases and health situations, for example lack of copper or zinc in plant nutrition may often lead to lack of the same element for animals.

For quite a long time it has been known that endemic diseases exist in Norway owing to environmental factors. Lack of phosphorus in animal nutrition in certain areas of the southernmost part of Norway is an example of such conditions. This has already been discussed in the nineteenth-century literature.

Lack of copper and cobalt in animal nutrition has been discussed by Engdal & Ulvesli (1942), by Ender (1942, 1944, 1946), and by Ender & Tananger (1946). Very small amounts of these elements are found especially in the fodder grown on organic soils, or on sandy soils that were originally podzoliced, but in some cases the problems are connected to areas of calcium carbonate deposits of shell sand. In addition to lack of copper, lack of zinc has also been detected in one area (Dynna & Havre 1963).

In Norway it is often found that heavy metals have to be applied to obtain good crops from cultivated plants. However, naturally heavy-metal-poisoned soil have also been observed. Poisoning from lead is found in several areas (Låg & Bølviken 1974). It is also clear that the vegetation grown in such areas is especially rich in lead. Simple experiments have shown that animals fed on such plant material possess abnormal quantities of lead in their organs.

In addition to areas with lead poisoning, naturally copper-poisoned patches have also been detected (Låg & Bølviken 1974). It may be mentioned here that sheep killed by copper poisoning, the exact sources of which remain to be discovered, have often been reported (see e.g. Nordstoga 1963, Frøslie 1977). After a continued search for areas with natural poisoning of soils caused by heavy metals, we have found patches with a very high concentration of nickel, and other patches with more complicated poisoning due to, e.g., accumulation of both zinc, cadmium, lead, and copper (Bølviken & Låg 1977).

Pollution may cause high concentrations of undesirable matters. In the immediate vicinity of roads with heavy traffic there may be an accumulation of lead in the soil and in plants. The most comprehensive investigations of lead content in vegetation along Norwegian roads fortunately show comparatively low figures (Frøslie et al. 1975, Havre & Underdal 1976).

There are many cases in which industrial pollution is found to be a danger to health. For a long time it has been known that the discharge of fluorine compounds from aluminium factories may be of great consequence to animals (see e.g. Ender 1969, Flatla 1972).

Analyses of soil samples from Odda showed pollution from zinc, lead, cadmium, mercury, copper, arsenic, selenium, and fluorine. In investigations with food plants the content of heavy metals was found to be such as to require a warning to be given

13

against high dependence upon plant products cultivated in the immediate vicinity of the industrial centre (Låg 1975 a). The analytical figures had been compared with the tolerance limits introduced by FAO & WHO (1972, 1974).

Investigations of soil samples from areas in the neighbourhood of abandoned mining smelteries were carried out. At Røros, a high content of copper was detected, at Kongsberg Sølvverk a high mercury content, at Evje a high nickel content, and at Modum Blåfarveverk a high content of arsenic (Låg 1976).

Continued investigations in the immediate vicinity of Modum Blåfarveverk showed a high content of arsenic in the plants, but according to FAO & WHO, the concentrations were not so high as to involve any danger (Låg 1978).

From unpublished results of investigations it can be mentioned that soils heavily polluted by nickel and selenium have been found in Kristiansand.

The soil condition, is as mentioned earlier, influenced by the climate. During the last 25 years, Norwegian soil scientists have tried to elucidate the effects of chemical climate factors. An investigation started in the autumn of 1954 showed very wide geographical variations in the chemical composition of the precipitation (Låg 1963). In coastal areas of Norway the precipitation is, to a great extent, influenced by salts from the ocean. By analysing humus samples of uncultivated soils clear relationships to the composition of the precipitation were found. The content of exchangeable magnesium and sodium was relatively high in humus samples from the coastal areas, while calcium predominated in samples from the inland (Låg 1962, 1968a, 1968b, 1975b). Determination of chlorine, bromine, and iodine also showed comparatively high figures in samples from the coastal regions (Låg & Steinnes 1972, 1976).

After proving these relationships it was of interest to study the distribution of other elements. The continued registrations showed that the element selenium has a geographical distribution similar to that of the halogens (Låg & Steinnes 1974, 1978). A high correlation was found between the annual amount of precipitation and the selenium content of the humus. The discovery of these relationships is especially interesting, since selenium has received much attention recently in connection with nutritional

14

and pathological problems.

An attempt was made to develop quantitative expressions showing how the elements from the sea water influence the chemical composition of the soils (Låg 1978b). The sea-salt decrease index or ratio gives the distance leading to a decrease to 50% in the respective element. This decrease will be somewhat different for the various elements. Excepting shore areas, a decrease of 50% for many of the sea-salt elements in the humus layer appears to take place over a distance of about 50–100 km between the coast and inland in western Norway.

When planning the continuation of geomedical investigations in Norway, we considered a collaboration covering more extensive geographical regions, since detection of the considerable chemical influence of the climate has made it very desirable to include areas outside Norway for comparative purposes. Discovery of natural heavy-metal-poisoning of the soil has brought similar whishes. Many geomedical problems caused by pollution are more or less of the same character all over the world. More valuable results should be attainable by cooperation than by different projects in the respective countries.

In arranging this symposium we have planned, in addition to exchanging knowledge concerning important geomedical problems, to discuss the possibilities for international collaboration. The form of cooperation may range from participation in specific projects to the foundation of permanent organizations.

Acknowledgements. In preparing this paper I have received valuable information from Professors Jon Jonsen, Henrich Neumann, and Olav Sandvik, and research assistant Gunvor Nersten has helped in literature survey.

Literature

Bersin, T. 1963. Biochemie der Mineral- und Spurenelemente. Frankfurt am Main. 695 pp.

Bowen, H.J.M. 1966. Trace elements in biochemistry. London and New York. 241 pp.

Bølviken, B., & J. Låg, 1977. Natural heavy-metal poisoning of soils and vegetation: an exploration tool in glaciated terrain. Applied earth science, 86, 1977, B 173–180.

Dircks, W. 1879. Nogle Undersøgelser af Hø. Tidsskrift for Landmænd, 6, 1879, 240–251.

Dynna, O., & G.N. Havre, 1963. Interrelationsship of zinc and copper in the nutrition of cattle. Acta. vet. Scand., 4, 197–208.

Ender, F. 1942. Undersøkelser over slikkesykens etiologi i Norge. (English summary.) Norsk veterinær-tidsskrift, 54, 3–27, 78–127, 137–158.

Ender, F. 1944. Sporelementenes etiologiske og terapeutiske betydning ved spesielle mangelsykdommer hos storfe og sau i vårt land. Koboltmangel som sykdomsårsak. (English summary.) Norsk veterinær-tidsskrift, 56, 173–186.

Ender, F. 1946. Koboltmangelens betydning som sykdomsårsak hos storfe og sau belyst ved terapeutisk forsøk. (English summary.) Norsk veterinær-tidsskrift, 58, 118–143.

Ender, F. 1969. The effect of air pollution on animals. Air Pollution Procceedings . . . Wageningen . . . p. 245–254.

Ender, F., & I.W. Tananger 1946. Fortsatte undersøkelser over årsaksforholdene ved mangelsykdommer hos storfe og sau. Koboltmangel som sykdomsårsak belyst ved kjemiske undersøkelser av foret. (English summary.) Norsk veterinær-tidsskrift, 57, 313–331, 353–405.

Engdal, O.T., & O. Ulvesli 1942. Forsøk med mineraltilskudd til lam. (English summary.) Meld. fra Norges Landbrukshøgskole, 22, 1942, 535–590.

Esmark, J. 1823. Om Norit-Formationen. Magazin for Naturvidenskaberne, 1, 205–215.

FAO & WHO, 1972. Evaluation of certain food additives and of the contaminants mercury, lead and cadmium. Sixteenth report of the Joint FAO/WHO Expert Committee on Food Additives. Rome. 32 pp.

FAO & WHO, 1974. List of maximum levels recommended for contaminants by the Joint FAO/WHO Codex Alimentarius Commission. Rome. 14 pp.

Flatla, J.L. 1972. The fluorine problem in practice – poisoning in ruminants. Festskrift til . . . Knut Breirem . . . p. 37–50. Gjøvik.

Frøslie, A. 1977. Kobberstatus hos sau i Norge. Norsk veterinær-tidsskrift, 89, 71–79.

Frøslie, A., G. Holt, & G. Norheim 1975. Faren for blyakkumulering i husdyr som får sitt stråfor fra arealer nær hovedveger i Norge. (English summary.) Nordisk Veterinær Medicin, 27, 173–180.

Havre, G.N., & B. Underdal 1976. Lead contamination of vegetation grown close to roads. Acta agric. Scand., 26:1, 18–24.

Henschen, F. 1962. Sjukdomarnas historia och geografi. Stockholm. 287 pp.

Howe, G.M. 1970. National atlas of disease mortality in the United Kingdom. Revised and enlarged edition. London. 197 pp.

Howe, G.M. 1972. Man, environment and disease in Britain. A medical geography of Britain through the ages. New York. 285 pp.

Jacobi, G. 1930. Das goldene Buch des Hippocrates. Eine medizinische Geographie aus dem Altertum. Schriftreihe des Natura. Bd. 5. Stuttgart. 75 pp.

Jusatz, H.J. (Ed.) 1974. Fortschritte der geomedizinischen Forschung. Geographische Zeitschrift. Beihefte. 164 pp.

Kolderup, C.F. 1898, Fosforsyregehalten i Ekersunds–Soggendalsfeltets bergarter og dens forhold til benskjørheden hos kvæget. Bergens Museums Aarbog 1897. No. 9. 11 pp.

Kovalskij, V.V.M. 1977. Geochemische Ökologie. Biogeochemie. Berlin. 353 pp.

Lindeqvist, J. 1856. Optegnelser under en Landbrugsreise gjennem det sydlige Norge i Sommeren 1855. 28 pp.

Låg, J. 1962. Undersøkelse av skogjorda i Nord-Trøndelag ved Landsskogtakseringens markarbeid sommeren 1960. (English summary.) Jordbunnsbeskrivelse nr. 47. Medd. fra Det norske skogforsøksvesen. Nr. 64, Bd. 18, 107–160.

Låg, J. 1963. Tilføring av plantenæringsstoffer med nedbøren i Norge. (English summary.) Forskn. og forsøk i landbruket, 14, 553–563.

Låg, J. 1968a. Undersøkelse av skogjorda i Oppland ved Landsskogtakseringens markarbeid somrene 1962 og 1963. (English summary.) Jordbunnsbeskrivelse nr. 48. Medd. fra Det norske Skogforsøksvesen, Nr. 91, Bd. 25, 331–393.

Låg, J. 1968b. Relationships between the chemical composition of the precipitation and the contents of exchangeable ions in the humus layer of natural soils. Acta agric. Scand. 18:3, 148–152.

Låg, J. 1972. Soil science and geomedicine. Acta agric. Scand. 22:3, 150–152.

Låg, J. 1975a. Innhold av tungmetaller og enkelte andre stoffer i noen prøver av kulturjord og matvekster fra Odda-området. (English summary.) Ny Jord, 62, 1975, 47–59.

Låg, J. 1975b. Noen særtrekk ved jordsmonnet på Smøla og i lignende områder langs den norske vestkysten. Ny Jord, 62, 1975, 65–75.

Låg, J. 1976. Noen foreløpige data for jordforurensning inntil nedlagte bergverksanlegg. (English summary.) Ny Jord, 63, 1976, 4–6.

Låg, J. 1978a. Arsenic pollution of soils at old industrial sites. Acta agric. Scand., 28:1, 97–100.

Låg, J. 1978b. Decrease in the sea-salt content of the soils from the coastal areas to the inland. (Eleventh Congress, International Society of Soil Science. Vol. 1, 227–228.

Låg, J., & B. Bølviken 1974. Some naturally heavy-metal poisoned areas of interest in prospecting, soil chemistry, and geomedicine. Norges geol.

unders., 304, 73–96.

Låg, J., & E. Steinnes 1972. Distribution of chlorine, bromine and iodine in Norwegian forest soils studied by neutron activation analysis. Isotopes and radiation in soil-plant relationships including forestry, p. 383–395. Vienna.

Låg, J., & E. Steinnes 1974. Soil selenium in relation to precipitation. Ambio, Vol. 3, No 6, 237–238.

Låg, J., & E. Steinnes 1976. Regional distribution of halogens in Norwegian forest soils. Geoderma, 16, 317–325.

Låg, J., & E. Steinnes 1977. Halogens in barley and wheat grown at different locations in Norway. Acta agric. Scand., 27:4, 265–268.

Låg, J., & E. Steinnes 1978. Regional distribution of selenium and arsenic in humus layers of Norwegian forest soils. Geoderma, 20, 3–14.

Mason, T.J., F.W., McKay, R., Hoover, W.J. Blot & J.F. Fraumeni 1975. Atlas of cancer mortality for U.S. Counties: 1950–1960. DHEW Publication No. (NIH) 75–780. 103 pp.

Mikkelsen, T., & M. Aas. Hansen 1967. Undersøkelse over selen og muskeldegenerasjon hos lam i Rørosdistriktet. (English summary.) Nordisk Veterinær Medicin, 19, 393–410.

Mikkelsen, T., & M. Aas. Hansen 1968. Ernæringsbetinget muskeldegenerasjon hos lam. (English summary.) Nordisk Veterinær Medicin, 20, 402–419.

Nicolas, D.J.D., & A.R. Engan 1975. Trace elements in soil – plant – animal system. New York. 417 pp.

Nordstoga, K. 1963. Undersøkelser over en særlig form for kopperforgiftning hos sau. (English summary.) 9. Nordiske Veterinærmøde. København 4. – 7. juli 1962. Beretning, pp. 196–201. København.

Rimpau, W. 1934. Geomedizin als Wissenschaft. Münch. med. Wschr. Nr 25, p. 940–943.

Stenersen 1877. Benskjørhed (Cachexia ossifraga), dens Symptomer, Aarsager og forebyggende Behandling. Tidsskr. for Landmænd, 4, 1877, 29–39.

Thesen, O. 1876. Landbrugs-Ordbog . . . [Litteraturanmeldelse]. Tidsskr. for Landmænd, 3, 357–361.

Tuff, P. 1922. Osteomalacie hos storfe. 2. nordiska veterinärmötet i Stockholm 1921. Förhandlingar, p. 405–431.

Underwood, E.J. 1977. Trace elements in human and animal nutrition. New York. 545 pp.

Vogt, J.H.L. 1888. Norske ertsforekomster. V. Titanjern-forekomsterne i noritfeltet ved Ekersund—Soggendal. Archiv for Mathematik og Naturvidenskab, 12, 1–101.

Zeiss, H. 1931. Geomedizin (geographische Medizin) oder medizinische

Geographie? Münch. med. Wschr. Nr. 5, p. 198—201.

Ødelien, M. 1960. Kan gjødsling være årsak til hypomagnesemi og tetani hos storfe? (English summary.) Tidsskr. for Det norske Landbruk, 67, 1960, 353—371.

Aanestad, S. 1895. Foderets Indflydelse paa Melkens Fedtmængde. Tidsskr. for Det norske Landbrug, 2, 1895, 339.

Ånestad, S. 1897. Engdyrkning paa Øst- og Vestlandet. Tidsskr. for Det norske Landbrug, 4, 1897, 481—511.

Aarstad, H. 1910. Jordbunden i Sogndal og Hæskestad, Dalerne. Jordbunds-beskrivelse nr. 1. 28 pp.

Aarstad, H. 1912. Romen og benskjørheten. Tidsskr. for Det norske Land-bruk, 19, 1912, 310—316.

Geochemical Data.
A Basis for Geomedical Studies

Bjørn Bølviken, John Ek, Erna Kuusisto

Large scale regional geochemical mapping based òn chemical analysis of samples of soil, stream and lake sediments, water, bedrock and vegetation is carried out by the geological surveys of Finland, Norway and Sweden. The obtained geochemical maps show that in addition to local geochemical anomalies, which may indicate interesting mineral deposits in the bedrock, there exist large regional provinces characterized by relatively low or high contents of chemical elements. Example of such provinces are given. Their existence suggests that geochemical maps could be used in geomedical research.

Modern prospecting utilizes a variety of geological, geophysical and geochemical methods, of which the geochemical ones are of particular interest in geomedicine. Geochemical exploration, which nowadays is accepted as an important prospecting tool by both governmental institutions and private industry, involves mapping on regional and local scales of the contents of chemical elements in natural geological material. The aim is to delineate geochemical anomalies, which are the effects of mineral deposits on the natural environment.

An interesting question then arises: To what extent can geochemical maps and other geochemical data, which were originally prepared or collected for prospecting purposes, be utilized in geomedical research? The present paper tries to throw light upon this problem by showing the type and amount of geochemical data, as well as examples of geochemical results, that the geological surveys of Finland, Norway and Sweden can provide.

Of the geochemical samples collected in the 1970s by these three geological surveys, soil and drainage samples are the prominent types (Table 1); samples of lake sediments, water, vegetation and bedrock are less used.

Table 1. Number of geochemical exploration samples collected by the geological surveys in Finland (GF), Norway (NGU), and Sweden (SGU), 1971–77.

	GF	NGU	SGU	Total
Soil samples (till, humus)	289,211	19,519	90,789	399,519
Drainage samples (organic and inorganic)	103,694	37,682	104,652	246,028
Lake sediments	6,383	1,771	–	8,154
Water	–	99	7,585	7,684
Vegetation	–	1,012	8,178	9,190
Bedrock	11,644	2,884	2,791	17,319

The greater part of the nearly 400,000 soil samples consists of till collected in Finland as part of an extensive program initiated in 1971 with the aim of covering large parts of the country with a density of 10 samples per km^2 (Kauranne 1975, Stigzelius 1977).

The drainage samples are of two kinds: 1) organic-rich material (ooze) from stream beds (Brundin and Nairis 1972), and 2) mainly inorganic active stream sediments (Bølviken et al. 1977); the first type prevails in Finland and Sweden, and the second in Norway. The sampling density varies between 0.1 and 5 samples per km^2.

The fine fractions of the samples (in most cases minus 60 or minus 180 micron) are analyzed for major and minor constituents using atomic absorption, optical emission, and X-ray spectrometry, as well as delayed neutron activation, colorimetric and fluorimetric methods. Cu, Pb and Zn are practically always determined, but in many cases up to 30 elements or more can be analyzed simultaneously. A typical suite of 17 elements from the Finish till survey is: Si, Al, Fe, Mg, Ca, Na, F, Ti, V, Cr, Mn, Co, Ni, Cu,

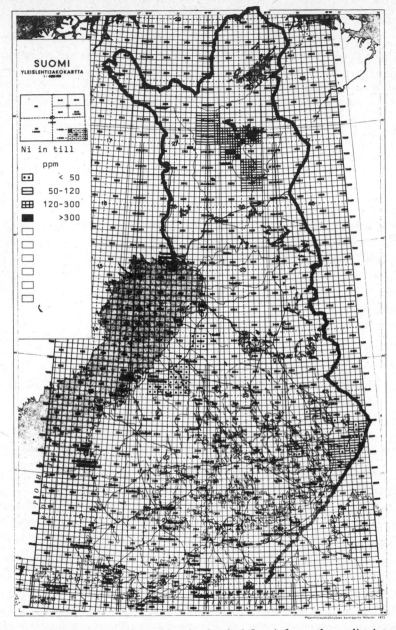

Fig. 1. Nickel in glacial till (sample depth 1.5 m) from three districts in Finland. The concentrations are computed as average Ni content per 100 km² map sheet.

Zn, Pb and Ag. However, at all three institutions, most of the samples are stored, thus making it possible to analyze them for other elements if so required in the future.

The results of these surveys show that in addition to local geochemical anomalies there exist large regional geochemical provinces characterized by particularly low or high contents of chemical elements, individually or in combination. Three examples of such provinces, one from Finland, one from Norway, and one from Sweden, are presented below.

Fig. 1 shows the regional distribution of nickel in till from three districts in Finland, computed as the average Ni content per 100 km². In the Vaasa district of western Finland the Ni content of the till is uniformly low (less than 50 ppm), while the Pohjois-Karjala district shows 50-120 ppm as the predominating concentration. The Lapland district forms a marked high Ni area; there the Ni concentrations in the till are generally more than 120 ppm, several entire map-sheets showing more than 6 times the prevailing concentration in the Vasa district.

In the Oslo region, Norway, which geologically constitutes part of a Permian graben, the stream sediments have much higher contents of cadmium and molybdenum than the sediments from the surrounding areas of Precambrian rocks. Cd is enriched by a

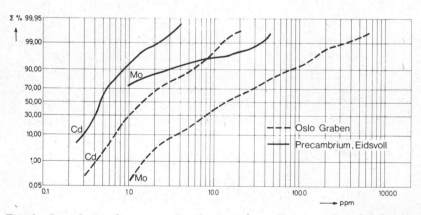

Fig. 2. Cumulative frequency distributions for cadmium and molybdenum in stream sediments from an area at Hurdal, with Permian rocks of the Oslo graben (364 samples, 700 km²), and from an area representing the surrounding Precambrian rocks (Eidsvoll 55 samples, 300 km²).

24

factor of approximately 5 and Mo by a factor of 10 (Fig. 2). It is interesting to note that these regional geochemical element enrichments — one element of which is supposed to be hazardous and the other essential — occur in one of the most densely populated areas in Norway.

A Swedish example from the Skellefte region showing an area of high arsenic is demonstrated in Fig. 3. While the normal content of As in humic drainage material from the region is less than 100 ppm, high As concentrations of up to 1400 ppm prevail over an area of more than 100 km² just north-west of the township of Boliden. This As province is considered to reflect the exceptional composition of some of the rocks in the Skellefte region, which is one of the most important ore provinces in Sweden.

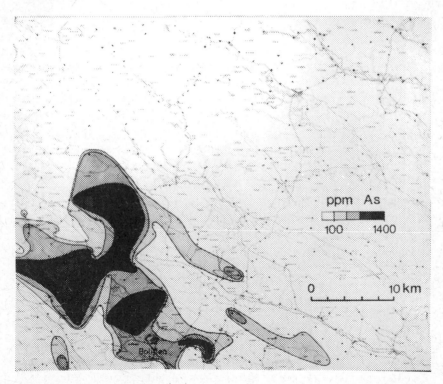

Fig. 3. Arsenic in organic drainage material from the Skellefte district, Sweden. The general As-background of the area is less than 100 ppm, only the values above this threshold are contoured.

It should be emphasized that the three examples of geochemical provinces demonstrated above, as well as many others found in the Nordic countries, are most likely natural occurrences. They must have been in existence well before people inhabited the areas, and are not thought to be influenced by artifical contamination to any appreciable degree. This feature, together with the fact that all the data, sample coordinates included, are or will be readily available on magnetic tape, has led the authors to believe that this type of geochemical information can be a valuable tool in geomedical research.

We anticipate that geochemical mapping will be accepted as a multi-purpose discipline which can provide basic data not only for exploration, but also for environmental research, agriculture, areal planning, and last but not least, geomedicine.

Literature

Kvalheim, A. (ed.) 1967. Geochemical prospecting in Fennoscandia. New York, 350 p.

Kauranne, L.K. (ed.) 1975. Conceptual models in exploration geochemistry. Norden 1975. J. Geochem. Explor. 5, No 3, 420 p.

These two monographs contain or give reference to the major part of the geochemical exploration litterature from Finland, Norway and Sweden. Other relevant publications not refered to in the monographs and references cited in the present paper are listed below.

Adamek, P.M., and M. Wilson. 1975. A new uranium province from the Precambrium of Scandinavia (abstract). In: Europe, from crust to core; Geol. Soc. Lond. Univ. Reading.

Armands, G., 1972. Caledonian geology and uranium bearing rock strata in the Tåsjö lake area, Sweden. Geol. Fören. Förhandl., 94, p. 321–345.

Armands, G., 1972. Geochemical studies of Uranium, Molybdenum and Vanadium in a Swedish alum shale. Stockholm Univ. Contrib. in Geol., 27, 148 p.

Armands, G., and S. Landegren. 1960. Geochemical prospecting for uranium in northern Sweden. The enrichment of uranium in peat. In: Marmo, V. and M. Puranen, (Eds.) Geological results of applied geochemistry and physics. Sect. 2 XXI. J. Geol. Congr., p. 51–66.

Björklund, A.J., 1971. Re-evaluation of ore potential at Korsnäs, Finland, by means of geochemistry. In: Davis, G.R. (Ed.), Prospecting in areas of glaciated terrain. Inst. Min. Met., London, p. 56–62.

Björklund, A.J., 1971. Sources and reduction of metal-content variation in biogeochemical prospecting. Geol. Surv. Finland, Bull, 251, 42 p.

Björklund, A.J., M. Tenhola, R. Rosenberg. 1976. Regional geochemical uranium prospecting in Finland. In: Exploration for uranium deposits. Intern. Atomic. Energy Agency, Vienna, p. 283—295.

Bjørlykke, A., B. Bølviken, K.S. Heier, I. Lindahl, and R. Sinding-Larsen. 1975. The Caledonian front in Norway: A metallogenic province. Abstract. Meeting of European Geological Societies Reading, U.K. 8—12 September 1975.

Botbol, J.M., R. Sinding-Larsen, R.B. McCammon, and G.B. Gott. 1978. A regionalized multivariate approach to target selection in geochemical exploration: Econ. Geol., 73, p. 534—546.

Brinck, J.W., and A. Hofman. 1964. The distribution of beryllium in the Oslo region — Norway — a geochemical, stream sediment study. Econ. Geol., 59, p. 79—96.

Brotzen, O., A. Danielson, J. Ek, and B. Nairis. 1967. Geochemical prospecting by the Geological Survey of Sweden. In: Cameron, E. (Ed.) Procedings Symp. Geochem. Prospecting. Ottawa April 1966. Geol. Surv. Can. Pap., 66—54, p. 44—71.

Brundin, N.H., 1973. Geochemical exploration for ores. Spex. Speaker, Queen's Village, 18, No 3, p. 1—6.

Brundin, N.H., and B. Nairis. 1972. Alternative sample types in regional geochemical prospecting. J. Geochem. Explor., 7, p. 1—19.

Brundin, N.H., and C.-A. Nilsson. 1973. Legeringsmetaller i Sverige — produktion och prospektering. Jernkontorets Ann. 157, p. 61—80.

Bølviken, B., 1965. Noen erfaringer fra geokjemisk malmleting i Norge. (Some experiences from geochemical prospecting in Norway.) Abstract of paper given at VI Nordiske geologiske vintermøte i Trondheim, January 1964. Norsk geol. tidsskrift, 45, p. 138.

Bølviken, B., 1969. Geokjemiske metoder ved leting etter bly langs fjellranden. (Geochemical methods for exploration of lead along the Caledonian front in Norway.) In: Jensen, R. (Ed.), Referat fra symposium i malmleting, NTH 13—14 January 1969, p. 89—95.

Bølviken, B., 1971. A statistical approach to the problem of interpretation in geochemical prospecting. In: Boyle, R.W., & J.I. McGerrigle, (Eds.), Geochemical exploration. Can. Inst. Min. Met. Spec., Vol. 11, p. 564—567.

Bølviken, B., 1971. Kan bly i naturen virke skadelig på mennesker og dyr? (Could lead in the environment have harmfull effects on human beings and animals?) NGU—NYTT, February 1971.

Bølviken, B., 1971. EDB i geokjemisk prospektering ved NGU. (ADP in geochemical prospecting at the Geological Survey of Norway.) In:

27

Lindahl, I., R. Sinding-Larsen, og F.M. Vokes, (Eds.), Referat fra det tredje malmgeologiske symposium. (Minutes of Third Ore Geology Symposium.) NTH, Trondheim, January 18–19 1971, p. 67–69.

Bølviken, B., 1972. Geokjemisk kartlegging av metallinnhold i bekkesedimenter. (Geochemical mapping of metal contents in stream sediments.) Underdal, B. (Ed.), Symposium om tungmetallforurensninger. Norges almenvitenskapelige forskningsråd, Norges landbruksvitenskapelige forskningsråd, Norges Teknisk-Naturvitenskapelige Forskningsråd, p. 71–84.

Bølviken, B., 1973. Discussion of Arthur W. Rose, 1972. Statistical interpretation techniques in geochemical exploration. Transactions SME/AIME, 254, p. 122–123.

Bølviken, B., 1973. Statistisk beskrivelse av geokjemiske data. (Statistical description of geochemical data.) Norges geologiske undersøkelse, 285, p. 1–10.

Bølviken, B., 1979. The redox potential field of the earth. In: Ahrens, L.H. (Ed). Origin and distribution of the elements. Pergamon Press, p. 649–665.

Bølviken, B., and B.A. Follestad, 1973. Geochemistry. In: Follestad, B.A.: Løten. Beskrivelse til kvartærgeologisk kart 1916I – M 1:50 000. Norges geologiske undersøkelse, 296, Skrifter 6, p. 27–32.

Bølviken, B., and C.F. Gleeson, 1979. Focus on the use of soils for geochemical exploration in glaciated terrane. In: Hood, P.J. (Ed) Geophysics and geochemistry in the search for metallic ores. Geol. Surv.Can. Econ. Rep. 31, p. 295–326.

Bølviken, B., F. Honey, S.R. Levine, R.J.P. Lyon and A. Prelat. 1977. Detection of naturally heavy-metal posoned areas by LANDSAT-1 digital data. In: Butt, C.R.M., and I.G.P. Wilding (Eds.). Geochemical exploration 1976. J. Geochem. Explor., 8, p. 457-471.

Bølviken, B., J.R. Krog, and G. Næss, G. 1976. Sampling technique for stream sediments. In: Kauranne, L.K. (Ed.). Conceptual models in exploration geochemistry. Norden 1975. J. Geochem. Explor., 5, p. 382–383.

Bølviken, B., and Ø. Logn, 1975. An electrochemical model for element distribution around sulphide bodies. In: Elliott, I.L. and W.K. Fletcher (Eds.), Geochemical Exploration 1974, Elsevier, p. 631–648.

Bølviken, B., and J. Låg, 1976. Naturlig tungmetallforgiftning av jordsmonn. (Natural poisoning of soil.) Naturen, 100, p. 11–16.

Bølviken, B., and J. Låg. 1977. Natural heavy-metal poisoning of soils and vegetation: an exploration tool in glaciated terrain. Trans. Instn. Min. Met., 86, p. B173–B180.

Bølviken, B., C.A. Nilsson, and H. Wennervirta, 1971. Summary of research and development in geochemical exploration in Scandinavian countries.

In: Boyle, R.W., & J.I. McGerrigle (Eds.), Geochemical Exploration, Can. Inst. Min. Met. Spec. Vol. 11, p. 11–14.

Bølviken, B., and R. Sinding-Larsen, 1973. Total error and other criteria in the interpretation of stream sediment data. In: Jones, M.J. (Ed.), Geochemical Exploration 1972, Instn. Min. Met. London, p. 285–296.

Dugerdill, Y., J. Ek, and F.C. and F.C. Jaffé, 1975. Use of mercury as a pathfinder for buried base-metal deposits in the Parkejaure area, Swedish Lapland. In: Jones, M.J. (Ed.), Prospecting in areas of glaciated terrain 1975. Instn. Min. Met. London, p. 1–6.

Ek, J., 1970. Geokemisk malmletning. Teknisk tidsskrift, 100, No. 11, p. 26–30.

Ek, J., 1974. Trace elements in till, vegetation and water over a sulphide ore in Västerbotten county, Northern Sweeden. Sver. geol. unders. Ser. c, 698, 50 p.

Eriksson, K., 1973. Prospecting in an area of central Sweden. In: Jones, M.J. (Ed.), Prospecting in areas of glacial terrain. Instn. Min. Met. London, p. 83–86.

Erämetsä, O., and I. Yliruokanen, 1971. The rare earths in lichens and mosses. Suomen kemistilehti, 44, Num. 4, p. 121–128.

Friedli, R., J. Ek, and F.C. Jaffé, 1977. Base-metal concentration in recent lake sediments and peat in Radnejaure area, Arjeplog, Swedish Lapland. In: Davis, G.R. (Ed.) Prospecting in areas of glaciated terrain 1977. Instn. Min. Met. London, p. 139–140.

Haapala, I., 1973. Haviantoja rapakivigraniittien tina – ja berylliumipitoisuuksista. (Observations on the tin and beryllium contents of the rapakivi granites.) Geologi, 25, p. 61–66.

Hattula, A., 1977. Geophysical methods in thick overburden, Kolari, Finland. In: Davis, G.R. (Ed.) Prospecting in areas of glaciated terrain. Instn. Min. Met., London, p. 120–127.

Hirvas, H., 1977. Glacial transport in Finnish Lapland. In: Davis, G.R. (Ed.), prospecting in areas of glaciated terrain. Instn. Min. Met., London, p. 128–137.

Hirvas, H., A. Alfthan, and E. Pulkkinen, 1972–1974. Annual reports of Project, Malminetsintää palveleva maaperätutkimus Pohjois-Suomessa. Archives of the Geological Survey of Finland (in Finnish).

Huhma, A., & M. Huhma, 1970. Contribution to the geology and geochemistry of the Outokumpu region. Bull. Geol. Soc. Finland 42, p. 57–88.

Hvatum, O.Ø., 1963. Oversikt over publiserte analyseresultater for mikronæringsstoffer i norsk jord og endel bergartsmateriale. (Survey of published analytical results for micronutritians in Norwegian soils and rocks.) Norges landbrukshøgskole, Meld. 42, Nr. 1, 42 p.

Hvatum, O.Ø., 1965. Geokjemisk undersøkelse av noen norske myrer.

(Geochemical investigation of some Norwegian peat bogs.) Abstract. Norsk geol. tidsskr., 45, p. 147.

Hvatum, O.Ø., 1971. Sterk blyopphopning i overflatesjiktet i myrjord. (Strong lead enrichment in the surface layers of bogs.) Teknisk ukeblad, 27, p. 40.

Hvatum, O.Ø., 1972. Fordeling av bly og endel andre tungmetaller i ombrogen torv. (Distribution of lead and some other heavy metals in raised bogs.) In: Underdal, B. (Ed.), Symposium om tungmetallforurensninger. Norges almenvitenskapelige forskningsråd, Norges landbruksvitenskapelige forskningsråd, Norges Teknisk-Naturvitenskapelige Forskningsråd, p. 59–70.

Hvatum, O.Ø., 1974. Jordbunnskjemiske undersøkelser i forbindelse med studium av feltmetodikk for geokjemisk prospekteringsarbeid. (Chemical investigations of soil in connection with study of field procedures in geochemical exploration.) Norges geologiske undersøkelse, Norges landbrukshøgskole, vol. I + II. 456 p., Vol. III. 150 p., Vol. IV + V diagrammes and maps.

Häkli, T.A., 1970. Factor analysis of the sulphide phase in mafic-ultramafic rocks in Finland. Bull. Geol. Soc. Finland, 42, p. 109–118.

Isotalo, I., 1971. Mangaanin kulkeutumisesta Uudenkaupungin makeanveden altaaseen. Vesitalous 1, p. 7–8.

Kataja, M., A. Nurmi, H. Wennervirta, & E. Vormanen, 1970. The data processing and the interpretation of the results in pedogeochemical exploration. Bull. Geol. Soc. Finland, 42, p. 151–164.

Kauranne, L.K., 1958. On prospecting for molybdenum on the basis of its dispersion in glacial till. Bull. Comm. geol. Finlande, 180, p. 31–43.

Kauranne, L.K., 1975. Regional geochemical mapping in Finland. In: Jones M.J. (Ed.), Prospecting in areas of glaciated terrain, 1975. Instn. Min. Met., London, p. 71–81.

Kauranne, L.K., R. Salminen, and M. Äyräs, 1977. Problems of geochemical contrasts in Finnish soils. In: Davis, G.R. (Ed.), Prospecting in areas of glaciated terrain 1977. Instn. Min. Met., London, p. 34–44.

Ketola, M., and R. Sarikkola, 1973. Some aspects concerning the feasibility of radiometric methods for uranium exploration in Finland. In: Uranium Exploration Methods, IAEA, Vienna, p. 31–41, discussion p. 41–43.

Kivinen, E., 1971. Suolamaista ja erityisesti sulfaattimaista. Suomalainen Tiedeakatemia, Esitelmät ja pöytäkirjat 1970, p. 135–147.

Kokkola, M., 1975. Stratigraphy of till at Hitura open-pit Nevala, Western Finland and its bearing on geochemical prospecting. In: Jones, M.J. (Ed.), Prospecting on areas of glaciated terrain 1975. Instn. Min. Met., London, p. 149–154.

Kokkola, M., 1977. Application of humus to exploration. In: Davis, G.R.

(Ed.), Prospecting in areas of glaciated terrain 1977. Instn. Min. Met., London, p. 104–110.

Lahermo, P., 1970. Om grund- och ytvattens kemiska geologi i Finska Lappland. Nordisk hydrol. konferens, Stockholm 27–29, Aug. 1970, vol. 2, p. 197–208.

Lahermo, P., 1971. Chemical geology of ground and surface waters in Finnish Lapland. Bull. Comm. Geol. Finlande, 242, 106 p.

Lahermo, P., 1971. On the hydrogeology of the coastal region of south-eastern Finland. Geol. Surv. Finland, Bull. 232, 44 p.

Lakanen, E., 1965. Trace-element levels in the vicinity of the Outokumpu copper mine (in Finnish). Ann. agr. Fenniae, v. 4. No. 4, p. 290–298.

Larsson, J.O., 1976. Organic stream sediments in regional geochemical exploration, Precambrian Pajala district, Sweden. In Govett, G.J.S. (Ed.), Exploration geochemistry in the Appalachians. J. Geochem. Explor., 6, p. 233–250.

Lindmark, B., 1977. Till-sampling methods used in exploration for scheelite in Kaustinen, Finland. In: Davis, G.R. (Ed.). Prospecting in areas of glaciated terrain 1977. Instn. Min. Met., London, p. 45–48.

Lundberg, B., 1973. Exploration for uranium through glacial drift in the Arjeplog district, Northern Sweden. In: Jones, M.J. (Ed.), Prospecting in areas of glacial terrain. Instn. Min. Met., London, p. 31–43.

Lysholm, C., 1972. Tungmetallinnhold i tang som en mulig geokjemisk prospekteringsmetode. (Heavy metals in seaweed as geochemical prospecting method.) Det store eksamensarbeid i malmgeologi. (Thesis). Norges tekniske høgskole, Bergavdelingen. 78 p.

Låg, J., and B. Bølviken, 1975. A natural pathway of lead from bedrock to herbivores. Abstract. International conference on heavy metals in the environment. Toronto, Ontario, October 27–31, 1975, p. C85–C87.

Låg, J., O.Ø. Hvatum, and B. Bølviken, 1970. An occurrence of naturally lead-poisoned soil at Kastad near Gjøvik, Norway. Norges geologiske undersøkelse, 266, p. 141–159.

Matisto, A., 1961. On the relation between the stones of the eskers and local bedrock in the area northwest of Tampere, southwestern Finland. Bull. Comm. Geol. Finl., 193, 53 p.

Mehrtens, M.B., 1966. Geochemical dispersion from base-metal mineralization central Norway. Ph.D. thesis, Imperial college, Royal School of Mines, University of London.

Mehrtens, M.B., and J.S. Tooms, 1973. Geochemical drainage dispersion from sulphide mineralization in glaciated terrain, central Norway. In: Jones, M.J. (Ed.), Prospecting in areas of glacial terrain. Instn. Min. Met., London, p. 1–10.

Mehrtens, M.B., J.S. Tooms, and A.G. Troup, 1973. Some aspects of geochemical dispersion from base metal mineralization within glaciated terrain in Norway, North Wales and British Columbia, Canada. In: Jones, M.J. (Ed.), Geochemical exploration 1972. Instn. Min. Met., London, p. 105– 116.

Nilsson, G., 1973. Nickel prospecting and the discovery of the Mjövattnet Mineralization, northern Sweden. A case history of the use of combined techniques in drift covered glaciated terrain. In: Jones, M.J. (Ed.), Prospecting in areas of glacial terrain. Instn. Min. Met., London, p. 97–109.

Nurmi, A., 1975. Geochemical exploration in a glacial ice-divide region: Riikonkoski copper deposit, Kittilä, Finnish Lapland. In: Jones, M.J. (Ed.), Prospecting in areas of glaciated terrain 1975. Instn. Min. Met., London, p. 54–59.

Nurmi, A., 1976. Geochemistry of the till blanket at the Talluskanava Ni-Cu ore deposit, Tervo, Central Finland. Geol. Surv. Finland. Rep. of investigation, 15. 84 p.

Nuutilainen, J. and V. Peuraniemi, 1977. Application of humus analysis to geochemical prospecting: some cases histories. In: Jones, M.J. (Ed.), Prospecting in areas of glaciated terrain. Instn. Min. Met., London, p. 1–5.

Often, M., 1975. Geokjemisk uran-prospektering i Njallav'zi-området, Nordreisa. Troms fylke. (Geochemical Uranium prospecting in the Njallaavi'zi area.) Det store eksamensarbeid i malmgeologi, (Thesis), Norges tekniske høgskole.

Padget, P., J. Ek, and L. Eriksson, 1969. Vargiträsk, a case history in ore prospecting, Geoexploration, 7, p. 163–175.

Rösholt, B., 1977. Case history of copper mineralization with naturally copper-poisoned areas at Raitevarre, Karasjok, Finnmark county, Norway. In: Davis, G.R. (Ed.), Prospecting in areas of glaciated terrain. Instn. Min. Met., London, p. 138–139.

Sinding-Larsen, R. 1968. En undersøkelse av de magnetiske og geokjemiske anomalimønstre knyttet til Skogen gabbromassivet i Bamle. (An investigation of the magnetic and geochemical anomaly patherns in the Skogen gabbro Bamle.) Det store eksamensarbeidet. (Thesis.) Norges tekniske høgskole.

Sinding-Larsen, R. 1973. Moderne numeriske metoder for geologisk klassifikasjon. Nytt fra Norgeodata, Nr. 1, p. 19–27.

Sinding-Larsen, R., 1975. A computer method for dividing a regional geochemical survey area into homogenous subareas prior to statistical interpretation. In: Elliott, J.L., & W.K. Fletcher. (Ed.), Geochemical exploration 1974. Elsevier, p. 191–217.

Sinding-Larsen, R., 1975. Statistisk analyse av geografisk fordelte data. In: Nytt fra Norgeodata, Nr. 2, p. 44–56.

Sinding-Larsen, R., 1976. Use of Landsat data in geological mapping and mineral exploration. Proceedings from Practical application of remote sensing. Alpbach. Austrian Solar and Space Agency, 1976, p. 63–66.

Sinding-Larsen, R., 1976. Et system for flerdimensjonal bearbeidelse av et geokjemisk undersøkelsesområde. (A system for polydimensional treatment of an area of geochemical investigation.) Dr.ing. thesis. Norges tekniske høgskole.

Sinding-Larsen, R., 1977. Comments on the statistical treatment of geochemical exploration data. Sciences de la Terre. Série Informatique Géologique, No. 9, 12 p.

Stendal, H., 1978. Heavy minerals in stream sediments, southwest Norway. Journ. Geochem. Expl. 10, 91–102.

Stigzelius, H., 1977. Recognition of mineralized areas by a regional geochemical survey of the till blanket in northern Finland. In: Butt, C.R.M., and I.G.P. Wilding, (Ed.), Geochemical exploration 1976. J. Geochem. Explor. 8, p. 473–482.

Stokke, P.R., 1968. En undersøkelse av den flybårne elektromagnetiske anomali i området omkring Lundamo, Gauldalen. (An investigation of the airborne electromagnetic anomali in the Lundamo area, Gauldalen.) Thesis. Norges tekniske høgskole.

Talvitie, J., and H. Paarma, 1973. Reconnaissance prospecting by photogeology in northern Finland. In: Jones, M.J. (Ed.), Prospecting in areas of glacial terrain. Instn. Min. Met., London, p. 73–81.

Toverud, O., 1977. Chemical and mineralogical aspects of some geochemical anomalies in glacial drift and peat in northern Sweden. Sveriges geol. undersökning. Ser. C. Nr. 729, Nr. 4. 37 p.

Vokes, F.M., A. Sindre, P. Eidsvig, and B. Bølviken, 1975. Geological, geophysical and geochemical investigations of the molybdenum – copper deposit at Langvatn, Setesdalsheiene, South-central Norway. In: Jones, M.J. (Ed.), Prospecting in areas of glaciated terrain 1975. Instn. Min. Met., London, p. 32–40.

Wennervirta, H., 1971. Geokemiallinen malminetsintä. Outokummun Sanomat, Vol. 35, Num. 4a, p. 26–28.

Wennervirta, H., and H. Papunen, 1974. Heavy metals as lithogeochemical indicators for ore in the Siilinjärvi and Aijala Fields, southwest Finland. Geol. Survey Finland. Bull. v. 269, p. 1–22.

Wennervirta, H., and P. Rouhunkoski, 1970. Lithogeochemical aspects of the Vihanti zinc ore deposit, Finland. Econ. Geol. 65, p. 564–578.

Woerns, N.B., 1976. Landscape geochemical investigations in the vicinity of a lead deposit at Snertingdal, Southern Norway. Master of science thesis, Brock University, Dept. of Geological Sciences, St. Catharines, Ontario.

33

Aspects of Geomedical problems from a Biogeochemical Point of View

Nils Herman Brundin

During the last four decades attempts have been made in different parts of the world, to locate ores by analysis of samples taken from vegetation (Biogeochemical prospecting). This has been done upon the assumption that the plants take up ampunts of heavy metals which are proportional to amounts in the ground.

The trials, which have been practically entirely limited to the aerial parts of plants, have only met with partial success. In many cases, it has been possible to find certain species of plants which reflect tha variations of a specific element in the ground and which can thus be used in prospecting for this specific element, but are unsuitable for other purposes.

The Geological Survey of Sweden has, however, in its prospecting activities had reason to investigate not only the aerial parts of plants but also the roots of plants living in a specific environment. This environment was the swampy banks along streams in northern Sweden with a relatively uniform vegetation, consisting of various species of sedge (Carex), sallow (Salix), and also water-clover (Menyanthes) and a few grasses (Deschampsia, Molinia).

Samples were taken not only from the plants but also from the ground in which they were growing.

Stream beds with known contents of several heavy metals were chosen for the investigation. The heavy metals included in the investigation were Cu, Pb, Zn, Mo, Co, Ni, U, As, and in at least one stream the contents of at least one metal was anomalous, in some cases highly anomalous.

It was found that, for all investigated metals and for all roots from different plant species, the content of the heavy metals was proportional to the content of the metal in the ground.

The aerial parts of the plants, however, showed a quite different behaviour, which has been shown earlier by Malyuga (1964) and Brooks (1972). At a low level of content of a heavy metal in the ground, the content of the heavy metal in the aerial parts increases with increasing content in the ground. At a somewhat higher level there will, however, be no further increase in the content of this metal in the aerial parts, even with a strong increase in the ground. This was found to be the case for all the investigated heavy metals in all the investigated plant species.

In one case, Pb, it was found that at a very high lead level (> 1000 ppm against a background of about 30), a new rise in the lead-content in the aerial parts occurred again. Probably other elements behave in a similar manner, but sufficiently high amounts of other heavy metals in the ground were not reached in this investigation.

The results of the investigation can be summarized in the diagram below.

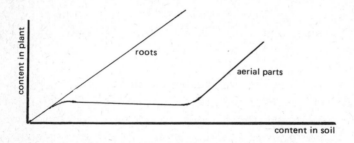

The results obtained in the investigation might illustrate certain aspects of veterinary-medical and human-medical problems.

A too large intakt of most (probably all) elements with food and/or drink will, for both animals and human beings, cause poisoning.

On the other hand, lack or deficiency of many elements (Fe, Ca, Zn, Co, Cu etc.) will cause deficiency deceases.

As both animals and humans depend in the last resort upon plants for food, it must be of importance to know how plants behave in geochemically anomalous areas in natural surroundings.

If one may venture to generalize about the results in the present investigation, the following conclusions of geomedical interest can be drawn.

1. There is small risk of grazing cattle and human consumers of the aerial parts of plants being poisoned even if the location of the plants is situated within a geochemical anomaly with considerably higher contents of heavy metals than is normal. In this case milk and meat from grazing cattle will, of course, also be safe for human consumption. Only with a very much higher heavy metal content than is normal will there be any risk of poisoning.

2. Roots from plants growing within anomalous regions will entail a much greater risk of poisoning.

3. If the contents of certain elements, however, are much lower than is normal (a negative geochemical anomaly), there will be a risk of deficiency deseases for grazing cattle and also for human beings living on local vegetarian and animal food.

The speculations here are tentative, as they are founded on a limited material from a specific environment. Further investigations seem, however, to be justified. They fall outside the direct sphere of interest for the Geological Survey of Sweden and should be conducted in co-operation with plant physiologists and agricultural institutions.

Environmental Carcinogenesis*

Ernst L. Wynder

Epidemiological research is providing increasing evidence that cancer is largely a man-made disorder and that it should, therefore, be susceptible to preventive intervention. (1—3) The man-made causes appear to be connected largely with our life-style, that is, smoking and eating habits, rather than with specific industrial factors (Fig. 1) (4).

It has been the principal function of the American Health Foundation to investigate factors that contribute to the causation of cancer in both humans and animals by an interdisciplinary team (Fig. 2). Such an approach provides us with an excellent vehicle to share ideas and communicate our findings.

The major actions and findings of our group may be summarized as follows:

1. Excessive tobacco usage continues to be the principal challenge of researchers in the area of cancer prevention. We have developed a school health program devoted to decrease smoking in adolescent children, and have tested a number of different techniques to determine how to most cost-effectively help adult smokers give up the habit. (5—9) We have also shown that long-term filter smoking appears to reduce the risk of lung and larynx cancer in smokers (10).

* This research was supported in part by National Cancer Institute grant numbers CA—17867, CA—17613, CA—16382, CA—12376, and Contract number NOI—CP—55666, in part by National Institutes of Health grant number RR—05775, and in part by American Cancer Society grant number R88.

39

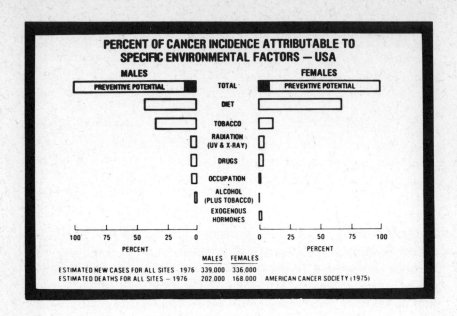

PERCENT OF CANCER INCIDENCE ATTRIBUTABLE TO SPECIFIC ENVIRONMENTAL FACTORS — USA

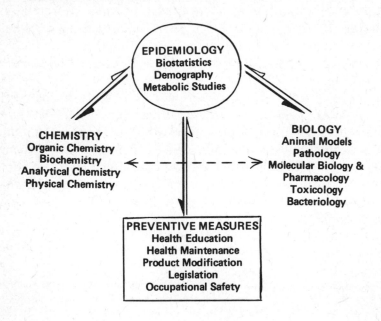

INTERDISCIPLINARY APPROACH TO CANCER PREVENTION

EPIDEMIOLOGY
Biostatistics
Demography
Metabolic Studies

CHEMISTRY
Organic Chemistry
Biochemistry
Analytical Chemistry
Physical Chemistry

BIOLOGY
Animal Models
Pathology
Molecular Biology &
Pharmacology
Toxicology
Bacteriology

PREVENTIVE MEASURES
Health Education
Health Maintenance
Product Modification
Legislation
Occupational Safety

2. We have shown that heavy alcohol intake enhances the risk of upper alimentary and upper respiratory tract cancer among smokers (11—13). This occurs possibly because of the nutritional deficiencies associated with alcoholism which enhance microsomal enzyme activity, which in turn enhances the function of the active form of certain nitrosamines (14—15).

3. We have evidence that ascorbic acid prevents the formation of nitrosamines in the stomach, and it is hypothesized that the low rate of gastric cancer in the United States may be related to the high consumption of Vitamin C with food intake (16, 17).

4. There exists metabolic epidemiologic as well as animal evidence that bile acids act as tumor promoters of carcinogenesis, the mechanism of which remains to be identified. The high bile acid content of feces appears to be related to a high fat diet (18—20). The carcinogen may be a function of the method of preparation, especially frying and broiling, of meat (21, 22). More research must be conducted on carcinogen(s) in feces (23).

5. Epidemiological studies have not revealed any single factor — with the possible exception of nutrition — that could account for the differences in breast cancer incidence between high and low risk countries (24—29). In the rat, a high fat diet has been shown to promote carcinogen-induced breast cancer, secondarily to increasing the prolactin/estrogen ratio (25, 30—35). In women, the peak prolactin output, which occurs at night, is increased by a high fat diet. Prolactin and estrogen have been identified in breast fluid of non-lactating women. Thus, breast fluid, which bathes the cells from which breast cancer arises, is also high in lipids (36—37). This fluid probably reflects much of a woman's environment and dietary intake. We are involved in an international study, comparing breast fluid from women in high and low risk countries (38). We hypothesize that the constituents in the breast fluid affect breast carcinogenesis.

The above describes some of the ongoing activities of our Institute in environmental carcinogenesis and cancer prevention. We hope that these studies will continue to identify factors implicated in human cancer risk, and that this knowledge will enable us to recommend measures directed to reduce cancer in humans.

41

Literature

1. Doll, R., Prevention of Cancer — Pointers from Epidemiology. London: Nuffield Hospital Trust, 1967.
2. Higginson, j. "Present trends in cancer epidemiology", Proc. Can. Cancer Conf., 8:40–75, 1969.
3. Boyland, E. "The correlation of experimental carcinogenesis and cancer in man", Prog. Exp. Tumor Res., 11: 222–234, 1967.
4. Wynder, E.L. and Gori, G.B., "Guest Editorial — Contribution of the environment to cancer incidence: An Epidemiologic exercise", J. Natl. Cancer Inst., 58: 4, 825–832, 1977.
5. Williams, C.L., Arnold, C.A. and Wynder, E.L. "Primary prevention of chronic disease beginning in childhood. The Know Your Body Program: Design of study", Prev. Med, 6:344–357, 1977.
6. Williams, C.L. and Wynder, E.L. "Motivating adolescents to reduce risk factors", Postgraduate Med., 54: 212–214, 1978.
7. Shewchuk, L.A., "Smoking Cessation Programs at the American Health Foundation", Prev. Med., 5: 454–474, 1976.
8. Schewchuk, L.A., and Wynder, E.L., "Guidelines on smoking cessation clinics", Prev. Med., 6:130–134, 1977.
9. Botvin, G.J., Dubren, R. and Batson, H., "A one-day smoking cessation program", presented at annual meeting of American Psychological Association, Toronto, Canada, 1978.
10. Stellman, S.D. and Wynder, E.L., "Comparative epidemiology of tobacco — related cancers", Cancer Res., 37:4608–4622, 1977.
11. Wynder, E.L., Covey, L.A., Mabuchi, K., and Mushinski, M., "Environmental factors in cancer of the larynx: A second look", Cancer, 38: 1591–1601, 1976.
12. Wynder, E.L. and Bross, I.D.J., "Etiological factors in mouth cancer", Brit. Med. J. I: 1137–1143, 1957.
13. Wynder, E.L., Dodo, H., Bross, et al., "Epidemiologic investigation of multiple primary cancer of the uppper alimentary and respiratory tracts. I. A retrospective study", Cancer, 24: 730–739, 1969.
14. McCoy, G.D., "Respiratory characteristics of mitochondria isolated from squamous epithelium of the hamster cheek pouch". Proc. Soc. Exp. Biol. Med., 156: 118–122, 1977.
15. McCoy, G.D., Hecht, S.S., Chem, Ch.B., et al., "Enhanced mutagenicity and metabolism of nitrosopyrrolidine by liver microsomes isolated from ethanol consuming hasters", Fed.proc. 37: 1471, 1978.
16. Mirvish, S.S., "Blocking the formation of N-Nitroso compounds with ascorbic acid in vitro and in vivo", Ann. N.Y. Acad. 258: 175-179, 1975.

42

17. Mirvish, S.S., "N-Nitroso compounds: Their chemical in vivo formation and possible importance as environmental carcinogens", J. Toxicol, and Environ. Health 2: 1267–1271, 1977.

18. Reddy, B.B. Narisawa, N., Weisburger, J.H. and Wynder, E.L., "Promoting effect of sodium deoxycholate and adenocarcinomas in germ free rats", J. Natl. Cancer Inst., 56: 441–442, 1976.

19. Reddy, B.S. Watanbe, K., Weisburger, J.H., and Wynder, E.L., "Promoting effect of bile acids in colon carcinogenesis in germ-free and conventional F344 rats", Cancer Res., 37: 3238–3242, 1977.

20. Narisawa, T., Magadia, N.E., Weisburger, J.H., and Wynder, E.L., "Promoting effect of bile acids on colon carcinogenesis after intra-rectal instillation of N-methyl-N'-nitro-N-nitroso-guanidine in rats", J. Natl. Cancer Inst., 55: 1093–1097, 1974.

21. Nagao, M., Honda, M., Seino, Y., Yahagi, T. and Sugimura, T., "Colon Cancer", Cancer Letters 2: 221–224, 1977.

22. Weisburger, J.A. and Spingarn, M., unpublished observation.

23. Bruce, W.R., Varghese, A.J., Furrer, R. and Land, P.C. pp. 1641–1646 in Origins of Human Cancer, Cold Springs Harbor Laboratory, New York: Cold Springs Harbor, 1977.

24. Alcantara, E.N. and Speckman, E.W., "Diet, nutrition and cancer", "Am. J. Clin. Nutri.", 29: 1035–1047, 1976.

25. Carroll, K.K., Experimental evidence of dietary factors and hormone-dependent cancers", Cancer Res., 35: 3374–3383, 1975.

26. Wynder, E.L., Cohen, L.A., Chan, P.C. et al, "Etiology and prevention of breast cancer", Recent Results in Cancer Research Vol. 46, Grundmann, E. (ed.), Heidelberg/New York: Springer-Verlag, 1978.

27. Wynder, E.L. and Hirayama, T., "A study of the epidemiology of cancer of the breast", Cancer, 13: 559–601, 1960.

28. Lilienfeld, A.M., "Epidemiology of breast cancer", Cancer Res., 23: 1503-1513, 1963.

29. MacMahon, B., Cole, P. and Brown, J. "Etiology of human breast cancer, A review", J. Natl. Cancer Inst., 50: 21–42, 1973.

30. Carroll, K.K., Gammal, E.B. and Plunkett, E.R., "Dietary fat and mammary cancer", Can. Med. Assoc. J. 98: 590–594, 1977.

31. Chan, P.E. and Cohen, L.A. "Dietary fat and growth promotion of rat mammary tumors", Cancer Res., 35: 3384–3386, 1975.

32. Chan, P.E. and Cohen, L.A., "Effect of dietary fat, antiestrogen and antiprolactin on the development of mammary tumors in rats", J. Natl. Cancer Inst., 52: 25–30, 1974.

33. Chan, P.E., Didato, F. and Cohen, L.A. "High dietary fat elevation of fat, serum prolactin and mammary cancer", Proc. Soc. Exp. Biol. Med. 149: 133–135, 1975.

34. Chan, P.E., Head, J.F., Cohen, L.A. and Wynder, E.L., "The influence of dietary fat on the induction of rat mammary tumors by N-Nitrosomethylurea: Strain differences and associated hormonal changes", J. Natl. Cancer Inst. 59: 1279–1283, 1977.

35. Chan, P.C., Head, J.F., Cohen, L.A. and Wynder, E.L. "Effect of high fat diet on serum prolactin levels and mammary cancer development in ovariectomized rats", Proc. Amer. Assoc. Cancer Res. 18: 189–193, 1977.

36. Hill, P. and Wynder, E.L. "Diet and prolactin release", Lancet II: 806–807, 1976.

37. Hill, P. Wynder, E.L., Kumar, P., et al. "Prolactin levels in populations at risk for breast cancer", Cancer Res., 36: 4102–4106, 1976.

38. Hill, P., unpublished observations.

On the Geographical Distribution of Malignant Neoplasms

Johannes Clemmesen

'Cancer' can only with difficulty be placed under the heading 'Geomedicine', since it covers a group of diseases, each of which is caused by sets of factors that may vary from place to place for the particular disease. For example, cancer of the stomach is frequent both in Iceland and in Japan -- both volcanic islands where people eat much fish -, but in these two countries the disease may well be due to different factors used for its preservation. It may be accidental that it seems to occur more frequently in the volcanic Kivu region in Africa than elsewhere on that continent (Oettle, 1964).

Generally, it may be said that the gradients in the incidence of most neoplasms are too steep to allow the demonstration of some overall physical factor such as temperature (Newell & Waggoner, 1970) or cosmic radiation, as recently suggested by Archer (1978). While it may be difficult to disprove that local levels of radiation may influence the occurrence of kidney cancer in the USA, with which he finds the closest association, the increasing trend for this cancer in Denmark must be due to something more powerful (Clemmesen, 1977a), and the appearance of mammary cancer on his list does appear less convincing, as will be explained later.

However, since the Oxford Symposium on the Geographical Pathology and Endemiology of Cancer in 1950, considerable information has been collected on the geographical distribution of cancer, providing several clues to causal factors influencing the occurrence of this group of diseases. Nevertheless, it is important from the start to point out some misapprehensions of the stratistical tables on incidence reported by the series of cancer registries now established in five continents.

The apparent uniformity of data collected from registries

working under medical systems of very different efficacy has led some authors to assume that the lowest rates observed, if combined, might enable us to estimate theoretically the preventable part of cancer cases, – according to Oettle (1964) 80% or more among Western races. Correspondingly, Higginson & Muir (1973) estimated 80–90% of cancers as due to external factors and thus theoretically preventable, and Doll (1976, 1977 a, b) in similar ways came to the conclusion that most, if not all, cancers are in principle preventable.

These principles do apply to most diseases, but inspiring to research as such editorial views may be, they are tragically inadequate for practical purposes. As pointed out by Morton Levin (1976) on the basis of personal experience of cancer registration in an industrial community, an estimate of 40–50% prevention of cancer would seem more realistic. Misinterpretations of the term 'external factors' as meaning external chemical factors and as applying mainly to industrial carcinogens have caused Higginson and his staff from *I.A.R.C.* 1978, to emphasize that in their estimate only 1–5 per cent of cancer in industrialized countries is due to occupational exposure.

In general it should be underlined that such use of statistical tables on cancer incidence will depend heavily on the medical attention available to elderly persons, not least in Africa, which contributes the data for 7 out of the 17 low-risk registries quoted by Doll. On that continent old people are considerably fewer than in industrial countries, so that rates for older age groups will be based on small numbers of persons and therefore subject to considerable variation by chance, but still deciding the issue in comparison with other regions (Davies et al. 1958 vs. 1962). It may be doubted whether any industrial country would prefer African life-style with its other hazards in order to reduce cancer risk, and it seems impossible, also theoretically, to reduce all cancers at the same time:

While there is no doubt that gastric cancer still shows high rates in Japan and Iceland, it is decreasing in incidence in most industrialized countries, probably because of improvements in food hygiene, such as refrigerators in stead of salting and smoking food. Nevertheless, this substantial decrease is mostly accompanied by a less marked increase in rates for colon cancer which

46

cannot be explained by improvements in differential diagnoses. (Clemmesen, 1977 a.) It seems therefore impossible to attain the lowest observed rates for both sites at the same time.

Similarly it appears that *cervical uterine carcinoma,* rarely found among Jewish women (Clemmesen, 1965), varies so much locally, e.g. in Copenhagen (Clemmesen & Nielsen, 1951), that it is difficult to ascribe the said rarity to any genetic factor. Contrarily, *mammary cancer* shows a weak, but definite hereditary trend (Jacobsen, 1946, Anderson, 1972) and increased frequency among women with an early menarche and/or a late menopause, as does cancer of the uterine corpus (MacMahon et al., 1973). Incidence of breast cancer has been associated with high fat consumption areas, and a clear social gradient unfavourable to the wealthy has been found in England and the USA, although not clearly in Copenhagen.

As pointed out by MacMahon et al. (1973), women who have born their first child before the age of 18 run only onethird of the risk of breast cancer confronting women who have their first child after their 35th year. How to combine the complete prevention of cervical cancer through virginity with the lowest possible rates for mammary cancer seems therefore a problem for the more distant future.

The association of *oesophageal carcinoma* with occupations exposed to alcohol has long been known (Registrar-General, 1934), and it is generally accepted that alcohol per se is without carcinogenic effect. Schwartz et al. (1962) found the risk determined by a combination with tobacco, perhaps with alcohol acting as a solvent. A comparison of data for Switzerland, England, and Denmark showing considerably higher rates for the first country suggests that consumption there is not restricted to visitors (Clemmesen, 1951).

Oesophageal carcinoma has presented various geographic riddles. In Transkei, South Africa, Burrell found places where this neoplasm occurred approximately 13 times as frequently as elsewhere. Cases plotted on a map were interpreted by Africans as giving the locations of their speak-easies, but intensive analysis of drinking habits failed to lead to definite conclusions (Oettle, 1964), although it has with reason been suggested that beer produced from maize contaminated with fungi or otherwise may play the decisive part.

Also in the Caspian Littoral of Iran (Iran-IARC, 1977) a significant increase in oesophageal carcinoma has been located, but even intensive effort has failed to identify the carcinogenic factor. It is in such cases that short-term in vitro tests for mutagenic qualities may, hopefully, be an essential help to epidemiology.

Bronchial carcinoma has rightly been ascribed to the smoking of tobacco, mainly cigarettes, although it is possible that other factors may be of additional significance in the individual case.

The estimate of a latent period of 20 years, originally postulated by Clemmesen et al. (1953) has been widely accepted. It follows that the study of correlation between tobacco consumption and incidence of lung cancer must be carried out over a 20 year period. This was possible only for the time when women did not contribute substantially to lung cancer cases so that tobacco comsumption was related to the male sex alone, as from 1930 to 1950.

The close linear relationship shown by Fig. 1 leaves but little possibility of any significant additional carcinogenic influence, such as from occupational factors not associated in some way or other with the carcinogenic effect of smoking.

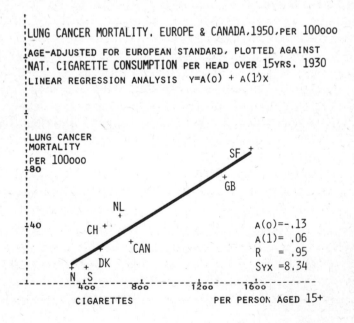

LUNG CANCER MORTALITY, EUROPE & CANADA, 1950, PER 100000
AGE-ADJUSTED FOR EUROPEAN STANDARD, PLOTTED AGAINST
NAT. CIGARETTE CONSUMPTION PER HEAD OVER 15YRS, 1930
LINEAR REGRESSION ANALYSIS $Y = A(0) + A(1)x$

LUNG CANCER MORTALITY PER 100000
80

SF
GB
NL
40
CH
CAN
DK
N S

A(0)=-.13
A(1)= .06
R = .95
SYX =8.34

400   800   1200   1600

CIGARETTES   PER PERSON AGED 15+

Nevertheless, it is possible that tobacco smoke may favour the carcinogenic effect of some pollutants of environmental character by paralysing the cilia or other cleaning functions of the air passage. Physical factors may also come into play. It seems that asbestos, which not only can cause mesothelioma but also, combined with smoking, increases the incidence of bronchial carcinoma heavily, largely depends in its carcinogenicity on its physical qualities, in particular the size of its fibres measuring 2.5 times 200 μm.

In Turkey, with a high mortality in two villages, roentgen examination has revealed many mesotheliomas. In the surroundings occurs a mineral, xenolit, with fibre dimensions similar to those of asbestos. In neighbouring villages where the dimensions of fibres are different the tumors do not occur (Sarracci, 1978). Even glass fibres of the said dimensions may cause tumors when injected into the pleura of mice.

Tumours of the urinary bladder show rather wide geographical variations in incidence. It is well known that in Egypt this tumour is supposed to be associated with bilharzia infestation of the bladder, although some additional carcinogenic factor may be involved (Clemmesen, 1965). It is less well known that in Turkey cattle have quite frequently been attacked by bladder tumours in some areas, owing to the presence of bracken fern, which contains compounds that provoke the disease when fed to cattle.

In industrialized countries bladder tumours are largely associated with tobacco consumption, although less closely than cancer of the bronchi. In England the disease has been reported as occupational in the dye and rubber industries, but incidence is still higher in Denmark, where no occupational association has been discovered, so far. Here, as in Norway and Sweden, the ratio between lung cancer and bladder tumours has for many years remained approx. 3/1, perhaps suggesting a casual factor different from England's or Finland's where the rates for lung cancer are far higher (Clemmesen, 1977a). The possibility remains, however, that a more moderate cigarette consumption than in England or Finland may leave a greater chance of avoiding lung cancer for the additional ten years, which make the average age for bladder tumours to occur.

It may be noted that while the overall lung/bladder ratio for the United States is close to the Scandinavian ratio, with an incidence close to that of Norway's, the ratios for individual states vary considerably. It seems possible that an analysis of ratios for individual states, if pooled according to dominating industries, may give some clues for the identification of causative factors (Clemmesen, 1977b).

In the study of the causation of *cattle leukemia,* geographical analysis has been particularly useful. This disease seem to have originated in East Prussia around 1900, and spred westwards, reaching the Rhine about 1914 and the Atlantic around 1939. For several years Bendixen (1963) had pointed out that epizootic cattle leukemia showed a highly uneven topographical distribution in Denmark, suggesting that it spread by a viral infection, and this view was finally vindicated when Olson et al. (1972) succeeded in demonstrating the virus.

For human neoplasms there have been very few parallels demonstrable on the basis of accurate cancer registration, but there may still be good reason to challenge the sceptical attitude to the possibility of viral etiology common at present.

International comparison of age curves for mortality and morbidity from leukemia show largely the same pattern up to the age of 60, except for Japan, where lymphoid leukemia is known to be rare — whatever the explanation may be. For older age groups there appears to be quite pronounced differences, but analysis of the development in Denmark shows that an increase in cases is limited to persons aged over 60, which seems to suggest that improved diagnostic facilities during the period between 1943 and 1955 caused a rise in deaths diagnosed as leukemia during those years. Data for morbidity for later years show a gradual increase in older persons.

In Africa Burkitt, originally on the basis of the cancer registry of Kampala, Uganda, demonstrated the irregular occurrence of the African juvenile lymphoma, which did not occur beyond the altitude of about 5000 feet, for which reason he suggested an association with mosquitos. The theory seems supported by the absence of the lymphoma in the lower Congo during the Belgian anti-malaria campaigns. Later the disease has been reported to occur there too (*Sympos. 1964*).

Furthermore, M.A. Epstein, who on my suggestion went to

50

Africa to study the virus environment, succeeded in demonstrating the presence of the so-called Epstein-Barr virus, which according to extensive studies seems related to Burkitt's tumour (Sympos. 1972).

A different neoplasm, the lymphoepithelioma of the nasopharynx, is also found unevenly distributed in Africa (Clifford, 1970) and has for many years been known to occur frequently among the Chinese (Sympos. 1967). In this case, too, the question is whether the Epstein-Barr virus represents a so-called fellow-travelling agent, or whether it is of causal significance (Henderson et al. 1977).

The absence of evidence based on cancer registration of an uneven distribution of malignant tumours in industrialized communities should not be quoted against the virus hypothesis for the origin of the said tumours, since it is possible that the virus transfer many require low hygienic standards and intimate contact (Clemmesen, 1970).

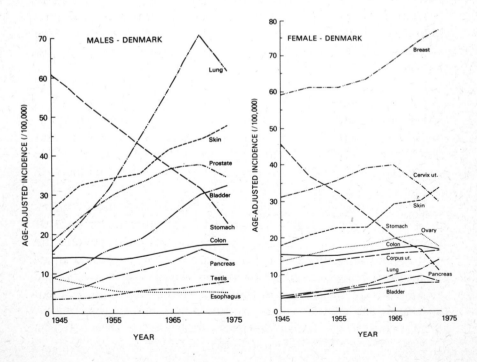

It should be realized that geographical distribution of malignant neoplasms must be considered for each site, at a given time and in a given geographical region. A review of Danish experience during 1943–1975 will show considerable changes in morbidity, suggesting where prevention may be possible.

It appears that skin cancer, which at present covers about 10% of cancers in each sex, is increasing because of increased exposure to sunlight. Among women about 30% of cancer are specific for the female sex, and while roughly 25% are accounted for by cancers of the digestive tract, only 5% are covered by the "tobacco cancers" of bladder and lung. An increase in these cancers, and in pancreatic cancer, may be expected if smoking is not discontinued.

Among males approx. 30% of cancers are located in the digestive tract, where a decrease is on the way, and grossly approx. 30% in the lungs and the urinary system, influenced by tobacco smoking.

It may therefore be theoretically possible to prevent perhaps half of Danish neoplasms if we consider the downward turn of the curves for gastric and cervical uterine cancer, the latter caused by screening procedures for initial stages. However, although occupational cancer should be in the first line of our attention we have, so far, no evidence of any substantial numbers of this origin.

References

Anderson, D.E.: A genetic study of human breast cancer. J.Nat.Cancer Inst. 48: 1029–1034, 1972.

Archer, V.: Geomagnetism, cancer, weather and cosmic radiation. Health Physics, 34: 237–247, 1978.

Bendixen, H.J.: Preventive measures in cattle leukemia: *leukosis enzootica bovis.* Ann.N.Y.Acad.Sci.: 108:1241–1267, 1963.

Blot, Wm., J. Fraumeni, & B.J. Store: Geographic patterns of breast cancer in the United States. J.Nat.Cancer Inst. 59: 1407–1411, 1977.

Bradshaw, Evelyn & Mary Schonland: Oesophageal and lung cancers in Natal African Males in relation to certain socioeconomic factors. Brit.J.Cancer: 23: 275–284, 1969.

Clemmesen, J. & Arne Nielsen: The social distribution of cancer in Copenhagen 1943–1947. Brit.J.Cancer: 5: 159–171, 1951.

Clemmesen, J., Arne Nielsen & Emmerik Jensen: The increase in incidence of carcinoma of the lung in Denmark 1931–1950. Brit.J.Cancer: 7:1–9, 1953.

Clemmesen, J., J.H. Maisin & P. Gigase: Cancer in Kivu and Rwanda-Urundi. A preliminary report. (Mimeographed.) 1962. Maison des Étudiants. Institut du Cancer. Univ. Louvain, cit. by Oettle, 1964.

Clemmesen, J.: On the probable role of oncogenic viruses in human epidemiology. Biomedicine, 15: 934–937, 1970.

Clemmesen, J.: Statistical studies in the aetiology of malignant neoplasms: Acta path. & microbiol. Scandin. Vols. I & II, 1964-65. Suppl. 174, 1964–1965. Vol. III. – Suppl. 209, 1969. Vol. IV. – Suppl. 247, 1974. Vol. V.– Suppl. 261, 1977a.

Clemmesen, J.: On the Epidemiology of Leukemia, in: Cleton, Crowther Malpas eds.: Advances in leukemia. pp. 1–50, North-Holland. Publ. Comp. 1974.

Clemmesen, J.: Correlation of sites, pp. 87–100, in: Origins of human cancer, Cold Spring Harbor Conferences on Cell proliferation. Vol.4, book, A, 1977b.

Clemmesen, J.: On cancer incidence in Denmark and other countries. Acta un.Int, ctr. Cancr.: 7:24–38, 1951.

Clifford, P.: On the epidemiology of nasopharyngeal carcinoma. Int.J.Cancer: 5: 287–309, 1970.

Davies J.N.P., Barbara Wilson & J. Knowelden: Cancer in Kampala. Brit. Med.J. 2: 439–443, 1958.

Davies J.N.P., Barbara Wilson & J. Knowelden: Cancer incidence of the African population of Kyadondo, Lancet II: 328–330, 1962.

Devesa, S.S., & D.T. Silverman: Cancer incidence in mortality trends in the United States, 1935–74. J.Nat.Cancer Inst.: 60: 545–571, 1978.

Doll, R.: Epidemiology of Cancer: Current perspectives. Amer.J.Epidemiology: 104: 396–404, 1976.

Doll, R.: Strategy for detection of cancer hazards to Man. Nature: 265: 589–596, 1977.

Doll, R.: Incidence of cancer in humans, in: Origins of human cancer. Cold Spring Harbor Conferences on cell proliferations. Vol.4, book A. 1–12, 1977.

Henderson, B.E., E.W. Louie, J.S. Jing, & B. Alena: Epstein-Barr virus and nasopharyngeal carcinoma: Is there an etiologic relationship. J.Nat.Cancer Inst. 59: 1393–1395, 1977.

Higginson, J. & C.S. Muir: Epidemiology, in: Holland & Frei: Cancer Medicine, p. 302, 1973. Philadelphia.

I.A.R.C.: Working towards the prevention of cancer. W.H.O. Chronicle: 32: 140–143, 1978.

Iranian-International Agency for Research on Cancer-study group: Esophageal cancer studies in the Caspian Littoral of Iran. Results of population studies. A prodrome. J.Nat.Cancer Inst. 59: 1127–1138, 1977.

Jacobsen, O.: Heredity in breast cancer. Copenhagen 1946.

Levin, Morton L.: Discussion on epidemiology of cancer current perspectives. Amer.J. Epidemiol. 104:405–407, 1976.

Mac Mahon, B., P. Cole & J. Brown: Etiology of human breast cancer. A review.J.Nat. Cancer. Inst.: 50:21–42, 1973.

Newell, G.R. & D.E. Waggoner: Cancer mortality and environmental temperature in the United States. Lancet I: 766–768, 1977.

Olson C., J.M. Miller & H.E. Hoss: Transmission of lymphosarcoma from cattle to sheep. J.Nat.Cancer Inst. 49: 1463–66, 1972.

Registrar-General's Decennial supplement, 1931. IIa Occupational mortality. H.M. Stationery Office, London, 1938.

Saracci, R.: Discussion on Manmade Mineral Fibres. Copenhagen 1978.

Schwartz, D.R., J. Lelouch, R. Flamant & P.F. Denoix: Alcool et Cancer. Resultats d'une enquete retrospective. Rev.franc. Étud.clin. et biol. 7: 590–604, 1962.

Symposium on Geographical pathology and demography of cancer. Oxford 1950.: Prelim.rep. J.Nat.Cancer Inst. 11:627–662, 1950. Final rep. Acta Un. int.ctr.cancer: 7:spec. no. (ed. Clemmesen). 1952.

Symposium on Lymphoreticular tumours in Africa (ed. F. Roulet). Paris 1963. New York, 1964.

Symposium on cancer of the Nasopharynx. U.I.C.C. monographs no. 1. (eds.) Muir & Shanmugaratnam. Copenhagen 1967.

Symposium on oncogenesis and herpesviruses. (eds.) Biggs, de Thé & Payne. Cambridge Engl. 1971. Int.Agency for Research on Cancer, Lyon 1972.

Comments on the Results of the First Finnmark Survey

Knut Westlund

Any search for a correlation may be performed with either the individual or the group as a statistical unit. The group may be the population of a large geographic area, such as a county, or of a smaller area, such as a municipality, or even parts of municipalities. In geomedical studies group data, rather than individual data, are characteristically used. There are, however, exceptions. For instance, Comstock examined the drinking water supply of individual infarction patients and compared the findings with those from the drinking water supply of individual controls.

The results of our cardiovascular surveys are compiled on different levels — counties, municipalities, and individuals. Most of the data may be considered peripheral to the theme of geomedicine. The diseases concerned have strong time trends, and the included variables are physiological, dietary, social, rather than related to soil and climate.

However, much has been written on the correlations that exist between the mineral content of drinking water and the death rates from an assortment of cardiovascular diseases. Our failure so far to include soil and drinking water data in the analysis is primarily due to the absence of adequate data. If, in the future, data on soil composition become available in a suitable form, they will be included in the correlations.

Even if the correlations based on individuals may not be of much relevance, they may serve to remind us of all the possibilities for confounding that exist in descriptive studies. Multiple regressions can probably only remove part of the confounding, and differences between areas with and without a soil factor may have to be large and consistent before we can confidently say that the differences are due to the soil.

For both males and females in Finnmark the serum cholesterol means are higher than in Sogn og Fjordane, corresponding well to the difference in mortality. The means for Finnmark males are also above those for males in the towns of Oslo and Tromsø.

Cigarette smoking is more common in Finnmark than in other areas, whereas there are only small differences in mean blood pressure.

Prevalence of previously recognized infarctions (questionnaire responses) is higher in Finnmark than elsewhere, corresponding to mortality statistics and the risk variable pattern.

Persons already under treatment for high blood pressure were fully as common in Finnmark as in other areas, including Oslo. Recognized diabetes, however, had a much lower prevalence in Finnmark than in Oslo or Oppland.

Means for municipalities in Finnmark differ more than can be ascribed to chance. The differences are smaller than had been hoped for, however, and so far have not been fitted into a sensible pattern.

Among the many individual factors that influence the risk variables and that may be unevenly distributed among municipalities and counties may be mentioned:

Ethnic group: Cholesterol is low in persons of Norse origin, compared to Lappish and Finnish persons. There is a distinct negative correlation between height and cholesterol in Norse and Finnish, but not in Lappish persons.

Marital status: Lapps are more often unmarried than other ethnic groups.

Physical activity: Cholesterol decreases with increasing leisure time activity, whereas the trend is the opposite for activity at work. Activity per se may have little influence on cholesterol, in contrast to triglycerides, which decrease with both leisure time and work activity. Blood pressure shows only small differences among activity classes.

Pregnancy: Cholesterol is higher and blood pressure diastolic in particular — is lower than in the non-pregnant women of the same age. Pregnant women smoke less.

Menopause: Cholesterol is higher than in currently menstruating women of same age. Cigarette consumption is higher.

The counties of Finnmark and Oppland have long differered in mortality from ischeamic heart disease. The risk variable pattern in the cardiovascular surveys corresponds to this difference. There is, however, also another difference between these counties: Mortality rates for 1951−75, compiled on the basis of both underlying and contributory causes on the certificates, were roughly four times as high in Oppland as in Finnmark from multiple sclerosis and pernicious anaemia. Special blood samples were therefore taken for trace element analysis in six municipalities in Oppland and four in Finnmark. The samples are being analysed at the Odontological Institute for Microbiology at the University of Oslo. The blood is afterwards used for a study of pepsinogen, related to a special study of gastrointestinal disease in the Finnmark municipalities.

Bibliography

Allwright, S., et al.: Mortality and water-hardness in three matched communities in Los Angeles. Lancet, ii, 1974: 860-864.

Bjartveit, K., et al.: The cardiovascular disease study in Norwegian counties. Background and organization. Acta med. scand., Suppl. 634, 1979.

Central Bureau of Statistics: Dødeligheten i fylkene 1971−1975. Norges offisielle statistikk A 948, Oslo 1978.

Comstock, G.W.: Fatal arteriosclerotic heart disease, water hardness at home, and socieconomic characteristics. Am.J. Epid., 94, 1971: 1−10.

Crawford, M.D., et al.: Changes in water hardness and local death rates. Lancet, ii, 1971: 327−329.

Forsdahl, A.: Living conditions in childhood and subsequent development of risk factors for arteriosclerotic heart disease. J.Epid. Comm.Health, 32, 1978: 34−37.

Glattre, E., et al.: Hjerte-kar dødelighet og hardt vann. Vann, nr. 3, Oslo 1977.

Leren, P., et al.: The Oslo study. Cardiovascular disease in middle-aged and young Oslo men. Acta med. Scand., Suppl. 588, 1975.

Meyers, D.: Ischaemic heart disease and the water factor. A variable relationship. Brit.J.prev.soc.med., 29, 1975:98−102.

Morris, J.N., et al.: Vigorous exercise in leisure-time and the incidence of coronary heart disease. Lancet, i, 1973, 333−339.

National Mass Radiography Service et al.: The cardiovascular study in Finnmark 1974−1975. Report Series, Nordic Council for Arctic Medical Research. Report 25, Oslo 1979.

Thelle, D.S., et al.: The Tromsø heart study. Methods and main results of the cross-sectional study. Acta med.scand. 200, 1976: 107—118.

West, R.R., et al.: Mortality from ischaemic heart disease — association with weather. Brit.J. prev. soc. med. 27, 1973: 36—40.

Westlund, K.: Distribution and mortality time trend of multiple sclerosis and some other diseases in Norway. Acta neurol.scand. 46, 1970: 455—483.

Zeiner-Henriksen, T.: Total og årsaksspesifikk dødsrisiko i relasjon til røkning og andre miljøfaktorer blant menn og kvinner i Norge. Tidsskr. Norske lægeforen. 98, 1978, 992—997.

Cardiovascular Disease Study in Norwegian Counties
Preliminary Report

Kjell Bjartveit

In Norway the National Mass Radiography Service, whose mobile teams cover the entire country, is responsible for tuberculosis screening. Since 1974 two of the teams have also been carrying out screening for cardiovascular disease risk factors. As in the tuberculosis programme, the local public health units are working together on this project. The study has so far been concentrated in three of our 19 counties, Finnmark, Sogn og Fjordane and Oppland, in which the people live mainly in small, relatively isolated settlements scattered over a wide area. The counties represent interesting contrasts in living conditions, however.

Death rates from ischaemic heart disease and cardiovascular disease vary considerably between the counties of Norway, and those chosen for the project are typical in this respect. Finnmark has the highest figures of all the Norwegian counties and Sogn og Fjordane the lowest, both for males and females. Oppland lies between these two extremes, but still at the lower end of the mortality figure distribution.

The *objectives* of the cardiovascular disease study are

1) an analysis of the pattern of risk factors within the three counties, related to the mortality of cardiovascular disease

2) an attempt to reduce the risk factors through
   a) an intervention programme among defined high risk individuals identified at the screening examination
   b) a health education programme covering the total population.

The efficacy of this programme will be assessed through

3) a follow-up study of cardiovascular deaths in the three counties related to

59

a) results of the screening examinations
b) results of intervention
c) trends in other counties.

In the three counties all persons, men and women, aged 35–49 years, and a 10 per cent random sample of men and women aged 20–34 years were invited for examination.

The screening started in Finnmark in 1974, and will go on in Oppland until the end of 1977. A total of 66,200 persons will be invited (Table 1). Invitation is by personal letter, and we have tried to arrange for the examinations to be as decentralized as possible. Altogether 480 localities in the three counties will be visited by the teams. One or two teams have been travelling by bus and working in premises rented for the purpose. In some coastal areas one team has been travelling by boat, with examination facilities on board.

The other side of the invitation letter contains a questionnaire which the person is asked to fill in and bring to the examination. This covers the history and symptoms of cardiovascular disease, together with details relevant to various risk variables.

The screening programme includes, in addition to the traditional miniature chest X-ray, the measurement of height and weight, checking of the filling-in of the individual questionnaires, measurement of blood pressure and a non-fasting blood sample which is centrifuged on the spot. Each day the sera are sent in specially constructed cooling containers to the Central Laboratory of Ullevål Hospital in Oslo, where they are analysed for cholesterol, triglycerides and glucose.

Before leaving the examination room residents in selected municipalities are handed a questionnaire on dietary habits to be sent in a pre-addressed envelope to our headquarters in Oslo.

The results of the screening examinations are collected at the headquarters, where the computer selects high-risk individuals according to defined criteria. The results of the screening examinations for each individual are sent to the local public health unit within two weeks, and they are then responsible for the follow-up examinations and the intervention programme. These three counties contain 70 municipalities in all, each having one public health unit. The local health personnel have been briefed on this study in special seminars held in the three counties.

The main principles for the follow-up examinations and the treatment and intervention programmes are that they should be based on the physician's own judgment and routine, and be performed within the capacity of the public health unit's daily work. Some guidelines are given in a manual, however. For the follow-up examination certain elements are mandatory, including a fasting blood-sample which is analysed for cholesterol. Pamphlets and other educational material have been produced for the intervention programmes.

The public health nurses have been active in this programme, and also in general health education on smoking and health and on low fat intake, visiting schools, clubs, organizations etc. The programme has been backed by the local newspapers and radio, and by voluntary organizations. It is also expected that the efficacy of general health education will be intensified through the ring effect based on the programme of intervention among the high-risk group.

Evaluation of the project is a lengthy process, and so far no results from the intervention programme are available. As a part of the evaluation, the high-risk individuals are called in for a new examination 12 months after the first follow-up, and once again values for the various risk variables are recorded. In addition, we will visit the county of Finnmark in 1977–78 for a new screening of the total eligible population.

Table 1. Cardiovascular disease study in Norwegian counties.

County	Time for screening	Total population	Population eligible for screening	Attendance percentage spontaneous	adjusted (see text)
Finnmark	March 1974 – Febr. 1975	78,000	17,400	83	95
Sogn og Fjordane	March 1975 – March 1976	102,000	16,600	90	98
Oppland	March 1976 – Dec. 1977	176,000	32,200		
TOTAL	–	356,000	66,200	–	–

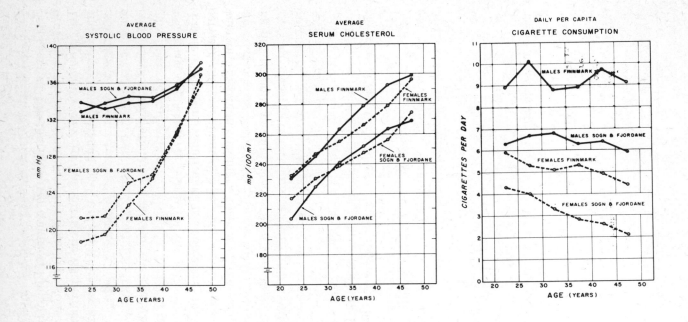

Fig. 1. Cardiovascular disease study in Norwegian counties. Preliminary results from screening examinations in Finnmark and Sogn og Fjordane. Risk variables by age and sex.

Some preliminary results from the *screening examinations* can be presented for the first two counties, Finnmark and Sogn og Fjordane, where a total of nearly 30,000 persons were examined. The *attendance rate* turned out to be 83 per cent in Finnmark and 90 per cent in Sogn og Fjordane. In many of the remaining instances we were informed, that the individuals concerned had recently moved from the municipality, for example. If this group is discounted, the attendance rates in the two counties were 95 and 98 per cent respectively (Table 1).

The average screening results for the three main risk variables (Figure 1) show no significant difference in *systolic blood pressure* between the two counties. The *cholesterol level,* however, is considerably higher in Finnmark than in Sogn og Fjordane. Among males aged 45—49 years the average figure in Finnmark was 299 mg per 100 ml, and in Sogn og Fjordane 269. The greatest contrast between the two counties was found in *smoking habits.* In Finnmark the per capita consumption of cigarettes among males aged 45—49, was 9.1 per day, in Sogn og Fjordane 5.9.

This article was prepared in 1977. A final report on the background and organization of this study has been published in:

Bjartveit, K., Foss, O.P., Gjerving, T. & Lund-Larsen, P.G.: The Cardiovascular Disease Study in Norwegian Counties, Background and Organization. Acta Med. scand. (Suppl.) 634, 1979.

Geographical Variations in Cancer Incidence In Norway

Knut Magnus

It is hardly generally recognized that the facilities for epidemiological research in cancer and other chronic diseases are out-
standing in Norway as well as in the other Nordic countries,
compared to most other countries in the world. The populations in our countries are rather stable, and all births, deaths,
internal migration as well as emigration and immigration are
centrally registered. The size of the populations is appropriate
for epidemiological studies, and indispensable positive and active
support is granted from the medical profession at all levels. Finally
the variability in the environment and living conditions within
and between countries provides a basis for interesting and fertile
areas of research.

The data to be presented here are based on the material of The
Cancer Registry of Norway. National cancer registration was started in Norway in 1952. According to rules laid down by the
Ministry of Social Affairs, all hospitals and institutes of pathology
are required to report all their cancer cases to the Registry. In addition, all death certificates on which cancer or tumour is mentioned are made available from the Central Bureau of Statistics.

The working conditions of the epidemiologist are quite different from those of the experimentalist. Firstly the epidemiologist
will not be the master of his own experimental conditions. He
has to accept them as nature and society creates them. Secondly
he will have to utilize material based on reporting from external
sources. The quality of such material may therefore be varying
and difficult to assess.

Epidemiological data may thus be subject to deficiencies as a
result of

a) Lack of specificity and sensitivity of diagnosis (false positives and false negatives)
b) Incomplete reporting
c) Erroneous or inconsistent classification

This paper will be restricted to the presentation of the incidence of certain types of cancer in urban and rural areas of six regions of Norway. Incidence, meaning the number of new cases within an area diagnosed during a specified period of time, is here expressed as the annual number per 100,000 of the population, adjustments being made for differences in the age distribution of the populations to be compared. The six regions are the following: the city of Oslo, Eastern Norway (counties nos. 01–02, 04–08), Southern Norway (09–11), Western Norway (12–15), Trøndelag (16–17), and Northern Norway (18–20). For the five latter regions results are shown separately for urban and rural areas as defined administratively.

The types of cancer presented here, which are listed in Table I, have been selected in such a way as to indicate the complexity in

Table 1. Reliability of geographical variations in incidence for selected types of cancer, and possible etiological factors causing the variations.

Primary site of cancer	Reliability of geographical variations	Etiological factors contributing to variations
Pancreas	Highly questionsable	Unknown
Breast	Questionable	Possibly Age at first delivery, Height-weight
Thyroid gland	Unquestionable	Unknown
Lung	Unquestionable	Smoking, Occupation?
Nose, nasal cavities	Unquestionable	Occupation (nickel exposure)
Malignant melanoma of the skin	Unquestionable	Sun exposure (UV radiation)

the interpretation of geographical variations in the incidence of this disease. In attempting to interpret geographical variations in cancer incidence, the prime question is whether the presented variations may be real or spurious owing to differences in diagnosis, reporting or classification. For cancer of the pancreas (Fig. 1) a high incidence is found in Oslo and in urban areas of Trøndelag. The excess is clearly statistically significant, but still it is far from certain that this reflects true variations in incidence of this disease. Pancreatic cancer may be very difficult to diagnose, and the variations may be a result of overdiagnosis in these cities, underdiagnosis in the other areas, or both.

For cancer of the breast (Fig. 2) Oslo and Northern Norway represent the extremes with the highest and lowest incidences. The material has not been so thoroughly analysed as to exclude completely the possibility that systematic errors may be responsible for the variations, but the variations would be in accordance with the hypothesis that women with an early age at first delivery and women of short stature and low weight constitute a low risk group for this disease.

Cancer of thyroid gland (Fig. 3) reveals particularly for females a distinct epidemiological pattern, the validity of which is beyond question. The incidence is markedly lower in the Southern and Eastern parts of the country than in the Western and Northern parts, and an excess is seen in rural areas compared to urban areas.

Fig. 1. Cancer of the pancreas in Norway 1966–1975. Total annual age adjusted incidence rate per 100,000.

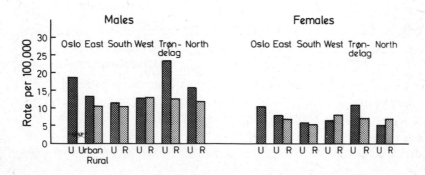

Fig. 2. Cancer of the breast in Norway 1966–1975. Total annual age adjusted incidence rate per 100,000.

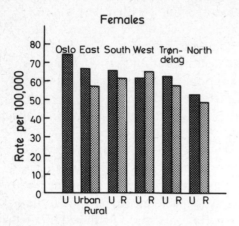

Fig. 3. Cancer of the thyroid gland in Norway 1966–1975. Total annual age adjusted incidence rate per 100,000.

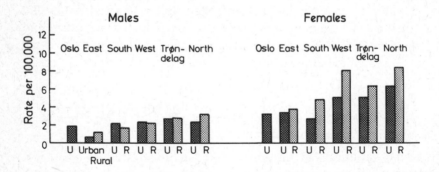

It must be admitted, however, that no wellgrounded hypothesis is at hand to account for those geographical variations.

The picture for lung cancer (Fig. 4) is similar to that appearing almost all over the world: very pronounced excess among males in urban areas, particularly in the largest cities. The main etiological factor is undoubtedly smoking. Regional variations in lung cancer incidence, although smaller than the urban-rural differences, are clearly statistically significant and correlate well with

68

Fig. 4. Cancer of the lung in Norway 1966–1975. Total annual age adjusted incidence rate per 100,000.

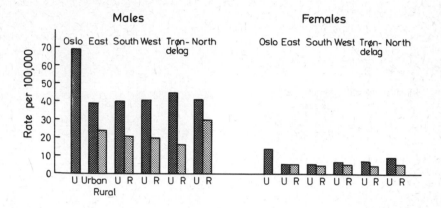

Fig. 5. Cancer of the nose and nasal cavities in Norway 1966–1975. Total annual age adjusted incidence rate per 100,000.

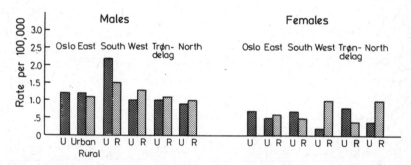

regional variations in smoking habits demonstrated in a survey among middle-aged males. Occupational exposure may also contribute to geographical variations in lung cancer incidence, but the quantitative significance on a total population basis can not be determined by the data now available.

An illustration of occupational risk is shown for cancer of the nose and nasal cavities (Fig. 5). In the urban areas of the Southern region the incidence is about the double of that in all other regions. This is due to the nickel refinery in Kristiansand. In collaboration with the factory the Cancer Registry made a special

69

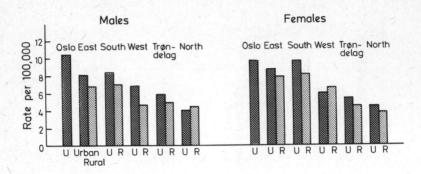

study showing that the risk of the employees of the plant was 25 times higher than that of the non-exposed population. The pattern shown in Fig. 5 is rather exceptional, and it is important to bear in mind that cancer of the nose and nasal cavities is a very rare type of cancer, encompassing only 0.3 per cent of all new cases of malignant disease.

Malignant melanoma of the skin is a tumor developing from nevi or from the pigment-producing cell, the melanocyte. A distinct north-south gradient in incidence is seen for this malignant tumor (Fig. 6), the incidence in the Northern region being only about one-third of that in Oslo and the Southern region. This pattern and the fact that the incidence of this disease has been almost quadrupled during 20 years (Fig. 7) has led to the hypothesis that variations in UV-radiation from sun exposure are responsible for these incidence variations in time and space. This hypothesis has been supported by more detailed analysis, in which the data have been grouped according to the site of the skin where the tumor develops.

There are many gaps in our knowledge of variations in cancer incidence and their possible causes. No doubt a lot of the gaps can be filled by intensified epidemiological research. It is indispensable, however, to cross borders in this research. It is very promising that a close co-operation has been established between the cancer registries of all the Nordic countries. There are other

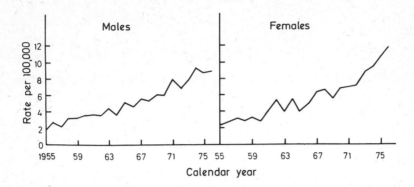

Fig. 7. Incidence of malignant melanoma of the skin in Norway 1966–1975. Total annual age adjusted rate per 100,000.

barriers, however, which we have been less successful in passing, namely those to other fields of science and medical research. I hope this symposium may stimulate the establishing of new lines of communication.

Data derived from: Geographical variations in cancer incidence in Norway 1966–1975 (The Cancer Registry of Norway. Published by The Norwegian Cancer Society 1978).

Selenium and Selenium-Vitamin E Deficiency Considered from a Geomedical Point of View

Mogens G. Simesen

The geomedical aspects of Selenium and Selenium-Vitamin E deficiency can, when we define geomedicine as that branch of medicine that has to do with the influence of climatic and environmental conditions on health, be divided into three main entities, namely:

1. Selenium Toxicity, its geographical factors affecting selenium toxicity.

2. Selenium and Selenium-Vitamin E deficiencies. Geographical extension and appearance.

3. Selenium's reputation as a carcinogen; the experimental data and the geomedical evidence, which now seems to show that selenium, contrary to its reputation as a carcinogenic agent, has an inhibitory effect on carcinogenesis.

Few, if any, of the microelements that are significant in nutrition have gone through such a dramatic conversion, metamorphosis, as has selenium. Selenium is the least abundant and the most toxic of the elements known to be essential for mammals (Schroeder et al. 1970).

Selenium was identified as the toxic principle of the diseases 'alkali disease' and 'blind staggers' in grazing livestock in parts of the Great Plains of North America early in the 1930s (Franke 1934). The acute cases of selenium poisoning − 'blind staggers' − show mainly sign of nervous system involvement with blindness, aimless wandering often in circles, and head pressing. The chronic poisoning − 'alkali disease' − is manifested by dullness, emaciation, lack of vitality, stiffness and lameness, loss of hair in mane and tail, and chronic nephritis and anemia.

The toxicity of selenium to animals varies with the chemical forms of the ingested Se. Localized seleniferous areas have been

73

Selenium — Vitamin E-deficiency — known manifestations in
different animals.

Species		Remarks
Chicken	Exudative diathesis	
Turkey	"White Gizzard"	OBS! Double Se-requirements
Rabbit	Liver and kidney degeneration Pancreas dystrophy Degeneration of heart and sceletal muscles	
Pig	Hepatosis Dietetica — HD (toxic liverdystrophy) Mulberry Heart Disease — MHD Nutritional Muscular Degeneration — NMD	
Horse	Nutritional Muscular Degeneration — NMD ("Käkmyositis")	
Ruminants	Nutritional Muscular Degeneration — NMD	

identified in Ireland, Soviet Union, Israel, Algeria, Morocco, South Afrika, Australia, Queensland and USA (Underwood 1977). All degrees of Se-poisoning exist. At low levels signs of Se-toxicity may take weeks or even months to appear.

With the exception of the so-called selenium-indicator plants, which accumulate high concentrations of selenium when grown on seleniferous soils, most plants take up only very low levels of selenium. Plants have no known requirement for selenium (Frost & Lish 1975). Selenium-indicator plants, accumulator and converter plants play an important role in the incidence of selenium toxicity in grazing stock, because they have the ability to absorb selenium from soils in which Se is present in forms unavailable to other plants. On their death the accumulator plants return Se to the soil in organic forms that are available to other plants.

The geographical extent of areas with known Se-toxicity is however much smaller than the areas now known to be deficient in selenium.

The earliest appreciation of selenium's function as an essential nutritient is associated with the findings by Schwarz & Foltz (1957) that minute doses of sodium selenite would prevent liver necrosis from occurring in rats fed torula yeast diets.

The roles of selenium and vitamin E in veterinary medicine were established in the early 1960s. It was demonstrated that both Se and vit.E protect biological membranes from oxidative degradation, that vit.E functions as a specific lipid-soluble antioxydant in the membrane, and that Se functions as a component of cytosolic GSH-Px (glutathionperoxydase), which reduces peroxides (Noguchi et al. 1973).

The levels of selenium in animal feeds and forages vary widely with the plant species and the Se status of the soils in which they have grown. Because there are wide areas in the USA, New Zealand, and the Nordic Countries where almost all the plants grown contain only low levels of selenium, several methods for providing Se-supplements have been developed (Gissel-Nielsen 1978). The methods of choice depend primarily on the conditions of the husbandry. The absorption of selenium from the feed and the distribution and excretion of selenium in the animal body vary with the chemical form of the ingested selenium, the dietary level, and the dietary level of several other elements such as arsenic and mercury. Monogastric animals have a much higher intestinal absorption of selenium than ruminants.

In the selenium-low areas a series of so-called Se-vit. E responsive diseases appear. In a variety of animal species various disease conditions have been shown to respond to Se-vit. E supplementation. In all species there is a tendency to degenerative disease of the striated muscles without neural involvement. This defiency syndrome has been described in lambs, calves, foals — typically young animals. In the USA the disease is called with muscle disease, in Europe nutritional muscle degeneration.

In pigs similar degenerative changes are associated with hepatotis dietetica and mulberry heart disease. In chicks the degenerative changes occur especially in the pectoral muscles and are associated with exudative diathesis. In turkeys the most characteristic sign of Se deficiency is degeneration of the gizzard muscle, white gizzard.

The third entity of the geomedical aspects of selenium is the

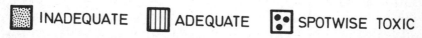

INADEQUATE   ADEQUATE   SPOTWISE TOXIC

Fig. 1. Generalized pattern og selenium concentration in crops for some European countries (Gissel-Nielsen 1977).

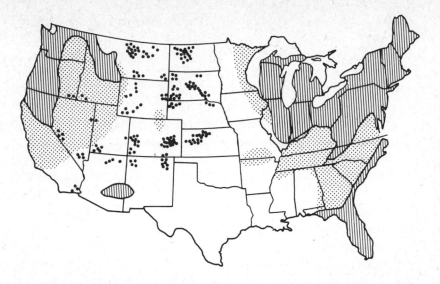

Fig. 2. *Regional pattern of Se concentrations in crops (Kubota et al. 1967) and Se concentrations in dry muscle of pigs produced at specific locations (Ku et al. 1972).*

Selenium in crops

    Low —   80 % < 0.05 ppm Se
    Variable — 50 % < 0.10 ppm Se
    Adequate —80 % > 0.10 ppm Se
    Local areas where accumulator
    plants contain > 50 ppm

Selenium in muscle of pigs

0.123 ppm in muscle (dry) of
pigs raised at locations indicated

From Allaway 1973.

alleged reputation of selenium as a carcinogen. Selenium acquired its reputation as a carcinogen in 1943 (Nelson et al.). Later experiments aiming to demonstrate or verify a carcinogenic effect of selenium have, however, been unsuccessful. On the contrary, evidence that selenium has an inhibitory effect on carcinogenesis has accumulated from experimental studies (Riley 1969) as well as from geomedical observations. Shamberg & Frost (1969) examined human cancer death rates in 10 of the cities from which Allaway et al. (1968) had reported Se blood levels. Allaway et al. had been able to demonstrate evidence of a geographic pattern reflecting the established regional differences in the Se levels in crops.

77

Shamberger et al. (1969, 1972) were able to demonstrate a high inverse relationship (r = −0,96) between blood Se-levels and human cancer death rates, and later to calculate the ratio of observed to expected cancer rate by organ site for males in 17 paired large cities in high-Se and low-Se areas of the USA. Particularly the mortality from cancer of the stomach, esophagus, and rectum was increased in low-Se areas. Further, when the data of Kubota et al. (1967) for the Se distribution in grains and forage crops were compared with the published female breast cancer mortality rates, the incidence was again shown to be higher in the low-Se than in the high-Se areas. Taken in conjunction with the animal experimental data it seems reasonable to suggest that selenium may actually be a cancerprotecting element.

Jansson et al. (1975) have recently shown that the mortality rates for cancer in the stomach, colon, and rectum show a marked geographical clustering, indicating that environmental factors may be significantly involved in the etiology of these cancers. The geographic dependency is highest for organs most exposed to the environment, such as organs linked to the alimentary tract.

Reference

Allaway, W.H., J. Kubota, F. Losee & M. Roth: Selenium, molybdenum and vanadium in human blood. Arch. Anviron. Health, 1968, 16, 342–348.

Allaway, W.H.: Selenium in the food chain. Cornell Vet., 1973, 63, 151–170.

Clayton, C.C., & C.A. Baumann: Diet and azo dye tumors; effect of diet during a period when the dye is not fed. Cancer Res., 1949, 9, 575–582.

Ehlig, C.F., D.E. Hogue, W.H. Allaway & D.J. Hamm: Fate of selenium from selenite or selenomethionine, with or without vitamin E, in lambs. J.Nutr., 1967, 92, 121–126.

Franke, K.W.: A new toxicant occurring naturaly in certain samples of plant foodstuffs. I. Results obtained in preliminary feeding trails. J.Nutr., 1934, 8, 597–608.

Gissel-Nielsen, G.: Control of selenium in plants. Disp. 1977. Copenhagen.

Harr, J.R., J.F. Bone, I.J. Tinsley, P.H. Weswig & R.S. Yamamoto: Selenium toxicity in rats. II. Histopathology, 1967, 152–178. In Symposium: Selenium in biomedicine. Westport, Connecticut.

Jansson, B., G.B. Seiberg & J.F. Speer: Gastrointestinal Cancer. Its geographic distribution and correlation to breast cancer. Cancer, 1975, 36, 2373–2384.

Kubota, J., W.H. Allaway, D.L. Carter, E.E. Cary & V.A. Lazar: Selenium in crops in the United States in relation to the selenium-responsive diseases of livestock. J. Agr. Food Chem. 1967, 15, 448–453.

Lakin, H.W.: Geochemistry of selenium in relation to agriculture. In: Agr. Handbook 200, U.S. Dept. Agr. Washington D.C. 1961a, 3–12.

Låg, J.: Soil selenium in relation to precipitation. Ambio, 1974, 3, 237–238.

Madison, T.C.: Sanitary report – Fort Randall. Statistical report on the sickness and mortality in the army in the United States. In: R.H. Coolidge (ed.), Senate Exch. Doc., 1860, 52, 37–41.

Mikkelsen, T. & M. Aas Hansen: Studies on selenium and muscular degeneration in lambs in Røros, Norway. Nord. Vet.-Med., 1967, 19, 393–410.

Mikkelsen, T. & M. Aas Hansen: Nutritional muscular degeneration (NMD) in lambs. Nord. Vet.-Med., 1968, 20, 402–419.

Nelson, A.A., O.G. Fitzhugh & H.O. Calvery: Liver tumors following cirrhosis caused by selenium in rats. Cancer Res. 1943, 3, 230–236.

Oksanen, H.E.: Studies on nutritional muscular degeneration (NMD) in ruminants. Acta vet. Scand., 1965, 6, suppl. 2, pp. 110.

Pedersen, K.B., & M.G. Simesen: Feed supplementation with selenium in relation to the vitamin E-selenium deficiency in pigs. Nord. Vet.-Med., 1977, 29, 161–165.

Riley, J.F.: Mast cells, co-carcinogenesis and anticarcinogenesis in the skin of mice. Experientia, 1969, 24 II, 1237–1238.

Schroeder, H.A., D.V. Frost & J.J. Balassa: Essential trace metals in man: Selenium. J. Chron. Dis., 1970, 23, 227–243.

Schroeder, H.A., & M. Mitchener: Selenium and tellurium in rats: Effect on growth, survival, and tumors. J. Nutr., 1971, 101, 1531–1540.

Schroeder, H.A., M Mitchener & Vt. Brattleboro: Selenium and tellurium in mice. Arch. Environ. Health, 1972, 24, 66–71.

Schwarz, K., & C.M. Foltz: selenium as an integral part of Factor 3 against dietary necrotic liver degeneration. J.Am.Chem.Soc., 1957, 79, 3292–3293.

Schwarz, K. & C.M. Foltz: Factor 3 acticity of selenium compounds. J.Biol. Chem. 1958, 233, 245.

Shamberger, R.J. & D.V. Frost: Possible protective effect of selenium against human cancer. Can.Med.Assoc.J., 1969, 100, 682.

Shamberger, R.J., S. Tytko & R.E. Willis: Antioxidants in cereals and in food preservatives and declining gastric cancer mortality. Cleveland Clin. Q., 1972, 39, 119–124.

Thompson, J.N., & M.L. Scott: Role of selenium in the nutrition of the chick. J.Nutr., 1969, 97, 335–342.

Underwood, E.J.: Trace elements. 4th ed., New York. 1977. pp. 545.

Multiple Schlerosis and Selenium

A review of the occurrence of multiple sclerosis and possible factors that might explain the geographical distribution of the disease, such as variations in the amount of available selenium

Gunnar Schalin

Our knowledge about the true prevalence of multiple sclerosis in the world is still inadequate also in most of the 'developed' countries. Most surveys probably underestimate the prevalence of the disease, and significant differences in case reporting also diminish tehir value in both national and international comparisons. Several general studies have anyhow proved beyond doubt that in the world as a whole the prevalence of MS can be related to the geographical latitude. The availability of selenium appears to be a decisive factor.

STATISTICAL DIFFICULTIES IN THE EVALUATION OF THE PREVALENCE OF MULTIPLE SCLEROSIS

The benign cases can be extremely difficult to diagnose. Even doctors are accustomed to believing that MS is a progressive and destructive disease, so that unless such a course develops the diagnosis MS is rejected (Hornabrook 1971). The correct diagnosis is usually made when other cases of neurological findings have been eliminated (Metropolitan 1975). Owing to the intermittent nature of MA, it can be assumed that many silent and benign cases of the disease are lost in the epidemiological surveys, especially in the less developed countries, and there also partly because of comparatively high costs for medical treatment.

The statistical material published reflects only a part of the desired total view of the distribution of the disease, even in countries with otherwise most reliable statistical reporting. In most countries there is no requirement by law to notify cases of MS (Leibowitz 1970). The direct cause of death rather than the underlying disease is often cited in the death certificates, and it has been found that 20–30% of all deceased MS-patients die of other causes than MS and/or its complications (Wikström–Palo 1976) — and are thus not included in the mortality figures.

It has been claimed that the current picture of the distribution of MS may thus reflect the distribution of trained neurologists, rather than the actual prevalence of the disease, because of the diagnostic difficulties. The similarities in the distribution patterns may seem to be striking, but significative differences can be observed. Multiple sclerosis has also been described as 'predominantly a disease of areas with high living standards' (Greenham and Peacock 1975) and it has been noted that 'areas with high prevalence are also developed areas' (Leibowitz 1970). The prevalence rates of MS do of course not only reflect incidence rates, but to a great extent also the quality of medical treatment, recording and reporting — and the general standard of living (where patients live longer the number of cases observed in the population is greater) — but in many cases facts defy these explanations.

No significant correlation has been found with standard of public health and sanitation (McCall et al. 1968), and more advanced training of neurologists togehter with more widespread information about MS to general practitioners have not changed the low prevalence figures for Japan (Kuroiwa and Shibasaki 1976). No cases of MS have been found among the Bantus of South Africa — who have full access to the medical facilities of the country — regardless of their varying standards of living (Bird and Satoyoshi 1975). In a great number of developed, industrialized countries patterns of distribution have been found that are definitively not correlated with either the distribution of income (or other factors related to the general standard of living) or the distribution of neurologists (or other medical facilities), e.g. in Finland, Denmark, New Zealand and partly also in USA (Wikström–Palo 1976, Hyllested 1956, Hornabrook 1971 and Kurtzke 1975).

THE WORLD-WIDE LATITUDINAL DISTRIBUTION OF MS

A majority of the scientists who have recently studied the distribution of MS have found a clear correlation with the geographical latitude. (McCall et al. 1968, Hornabrook 1971, Kuroiwa and Shibasaki 1976, Kurtzke 1975, Spillane 1972, Westlund and Kurland 1952.) According to McCall (1968) 29 prevalence studies plotted against latitude give a correlation coefficient of r=0,845 (with the exception of Japan) or a steady gradient of the disease with latitude. Alter et al. give the latitudinal distribution of MS plotted by computer as a parabolic function (1974). This may be right south of lat. 60°N, but hardly so in the north, at least neither in Scandinavia, where MS is rare in Lapland, nor in Greenland. In most national surveys gradients found have been in general linear and mostly compatible with the world-wide figures, with the notable exception of Japan (Kurtzke, 1975).

The recently published results of systematic surveys of MS in Asia (Kuroiwa et al. 1977) indicate that the course of the illness there is different from what is considered normal in Europe. More severe symptoms in the early stages of the disease may cause the illness to be discovered at a lower age-level in Asia. As a result of this, the low prevalence rates for Japan and several other Asian countries can not be rejected as 'only due to the age-structure' of the countries in question. The low rates of prevalence in Japan are strikingly different from the high rates in New Zealand on the corresponding latitude in the southern hemisphere.

THE FOCAL DISTRIBUTION OF MULTIPLE SCLEROSIS

The prevalence of MS varies not only with latitude, but also significantly within surveyed areas. (Swank et al. 1952, Hyllested 1956, Kurtzke 1965, Wikström and Palo 1975, Murray 1976). One of the best examples is Switzerland, where the illness in three consecutive, different studies has been found concentrated to one and the same limited area in the northern part – Basel, Baselland, Aargau, Solothurn and Zürich (Bing and Reese 1926, Ackermann 1931 and Georgi and Hall 1956 and 1957).

The foci on maps often, of course, do not represent true focal areas of the disease and are often merely areas where there are more cases of MS than we expect that there should be, but they are anyhow of the utmost importance as circumstantial evidence in the cases against suspected causative factors. There is no need to clarify the picture by trying to connect clusters of known cases of MS into continuous belts, as it ought to be quite clear that there can be more than one focal area in any country. As long as the causative factor (or factors) is unknown it can not be presumed that it will have any respect for administrative boundaries. It can of course not be taken for granted that 'a widespread geographical factor' could not also cause a local focal pattern.

DISTRIBUTION OF MULTIPLE SCLEROSIS RELATED TO PLACES OF BIRTH OF KNOWN CASES

In the discussion of foci and the distribution of MS only a few have reported cases according to domicile in early childhood, regardless of the fact that the hypothesis of childhood onset and long latency in MS is by now generally accepted (Kurtzke 1965, Beebe et al. 1967, Aller et al. 1966, Dean and Kurtzke 1971, Spillane 1972). Wikström and Palo have studied the clustering of known cases of MS according to places of birth and conclude that the risk of getting MS definitely varies with places of birth (1975). Increasing national and international migrations have by now made it difficult to identify high-risk spots and areas without relating the prevalence of MS to the childhood domicile of the patients.

THE VIRAL ETIOLOGY OF MULTIPLE SCLEROSIS

In some aspects the geographical distribution of MS suggests the operation of an infective agent. Some have rejected the notion as conflicting with their clinical observations, (McAlpine et al. 1955) but many have come to the conclusion that a viral hypothesis explains most of the epidemiological and experimental data on MS better than any other hypothesis currently available (Leibowitz 1970, Dean and Kurtzke 1971, Spillane 1972). The viral hypothesis is supported by evidence from many countries, e.g. the epidemic outburst of MS the Færoe Islands after 1944 (Kurtzke and Hyllested 1975), the laboratory personnel that were infected in the 1940s in the UK (Campbell et al. 1947) and the increases in the incidence of the disease in South Africa 1964—70 and in Tokyo 1966—72 (Bird and Satoyoshi 1975). The long period of 'silent' development between the time when the disease is 'caught' and the year of onset 5—25 years later is best explained with a slow-virus hypothesis.

THE ROLE OF ENDOGENOUS FACTORS IN THE ETIOLOGY OF MULTIPLE SCLEROSIS

Although it has been generally agreed that an exogenous factor may be implicated to explain the epidemiological findings, it is equally likely that some endogenous factor also plays a role in determining which patients exposed to a particular exogenous factor are susceptible to the disease or develop it. (Poskanzer et al. 1976). Endogenous autoimmune reactions may play a role as well as genetic factors. That is obviously the case on the Orkney and Shetland Islands where the extremely high and increasing prevalence of MS has been correlated to an equally high frequency of certain HLA-antigenes that may dispose to MS. The genetic factors can probably be decisive in individual cases (Kuroiwa 1975, Detels 1964, Wikström 1975) but it remains unlikely that MS should be a disease of predominantly genetic origin, considering the fact that the world distribution suggests the opposite. (Poskanzer et al. 1976).

The identical prevalence of MS among genetically different groups of native Israelis (of European and Afro-asiatic descent) indicates that the exogenous factors are decisive (Leibowitz 1970). Increased familial incidence has also been found to be the result of exposure to a common agent rather than inherited abnormality or predisposition (Poskanzer and Schapira 1963), and the rarity of conjugal MS can not be accepted as a counter-argument if we consider that MS is acquired before marriage (Kurtzke 1965).

POSSIBLE HYPOTHESES CONCERNING CAUSES OF MS

The world-wide distribution of MS has been found to be compatible with either of two hypotheses: 1. The prevalence of causative factors is not related to latitude but the prevalence of protective factors is inversely related to latitude — or 2. The prevalence of the causative factor is directly related to latitude, and there is an incubation period of a number of years between time of exposure and onset of symptoms, and that individuals become less

85

susceptible to clinical multiple sclerosis with increasing age at the time of the exposure to the causative factors (Detels 1976). The two hypotheses are not at all incompatible but on the contrary consistent (considering the fact that a causative factor may well in itself be prevalent without actual relation to latitude, and still at the same time associated with some other factor directly related to latitude). Swayback and scrapie among sheep are important parallel cases. Swayback is considered to be a nutritional disease, but is apparently in part caused by an infectious agent, and some strains of sheep appear to be less susceptible to the strongly infectious viral agent that causes scrapie.

AN INTRICATE INTERPLAY OF CAUSATIVE FACTORS

The cause of the enigmatic latitudinal distribution of MS seems to be a combination of innate endogenous factors and rather decisive exogenous factors, viral causative agents and environmental factors that may confer protection against developing clinical MS (Poskanzer and Detels 1976). The foci are best explained by exposure to a common environmental factor, either a viral infection or absence/lack of natural protection – or both. A decisively protective factor with a general world-wide prevalence inversely related to latitude can of course also at the same time be so unevenly prevalent locally, that it may cause such a focal pattern. The prevalence of clinical MS apparently mainly reflects exposure to environmental factors during childhood before 15 years of age.

THE DECISIVE ROLE OF SELENIUM

Among many such factors the most likely ought to be soil factors dependent on the balance between precipitation and evaporation and the soil formation, being correlated with latitude as is the prevalence of MS, factors that may just as well be related to diseases in man as in his domestic animals. Selenium appears to be the critical factor and lack of selenium may play the decisive role in the etiology of MS.

As with most micro-elements, the amounts of Se in soils is related to the amount in the parent rock, but with Se the amounts

86

are increased as a result of soil weathering (Wells 1967). On the other hand, where the soil contains soluble selenium compounds these are lost by the leaching processes, except where they remain linked to the secondary clay-sized minerals. Generally speaking, the more humid the area the greater the risk of inadequacy of Se in the soils (Johnson 1975).

AVAILABILITY OF SELENIUM INVERSELY RELATED TO LATITUDE

In the wide areas of the tropical and subtropical regions, where evaporation exceeds precipitation (dry sub-humid, semi-arid and arid areas) the soils can be expected to contain adequate amounts of Se. Outside the tropics evaporation is gradually decreasing, so that in the belt between 40 and 50 degrees of latitude it is already only half of the evaporation in the belt between 10 and 20 degrees of latitude (N and S) (Liljequist 1962). In these areas, where precipitation in general exceeds evaporation (moist sub-humid, humid and very humid areas) the leached soils can be expected to contain less than adequate amounts of Se in many areas, especially where the Se-content of the parent rock is low. Thus the amounts of Se in soils can be expected to be inversely related to the geographical latitude (as far as soil formation is dependent on the water balance).

SELENIUM-RESPONSIVE DISORDERS IN ANIMALS

Selenium is now recognized as an essential nutrient for animals. Several different disorders resulting from inadequacy of naturally available Se have been recognized in practically all the major livestock-producing countries of the world (Judson and Obst 1975). Many areas have been found to be deficient in Se through diagnosis of Se-responsive disorders in domestic animals, as it has been shown that Se concentrations in soils, pastures and blood of grazing livestock correlate closely with each other, and with areas within which Se-responsive disorders have been found. In the south-western parts of Australia such areas, where Se-responsive disorders in sheep have been observed, have also been found to correspond well with areas characterized by unusually low Se concentrations in pastures, (generally in the higher rainfall districts, associated with sandy soils) mapped by M.R. Gardiner 1969 (Godwin 1975). Similar correlated areas have been found in New South Wales, Victoria and South Australia (Lee 1975) and also in New Zealand, especially on the eastern half of South Island (Hartley and Grant 1961).

THE BIOCHEMICAL ROLE OF SELENIUM

Our present knowledge of the significance of the different roles of the trace elements and their interactions in the nutrition of both man and his domestric animals is unfortunately extremely limited. Through experiments on animals most of the recent achievements in this field have been made in veterinary medicine.

In 1973 Noguchi, Cantor and Scott presented a general hypothesis concerning the role of selenium, based on studies of inter-relationships in chicken tissues. The hypothesis recognizes the essential role of Se as a component of the enzyme glutathione peroxidase (GSH-px), that together with vitamin E is necessary for protection of mitochondrial and microsomal membranes from lipid peroxidation. It can well be assumed that their hypothesis can be applied to animal tissues in general (Goodwin 1975) and in part explain the role of Se deficiency in the pathogenesis of MS.

Shukla, Jensen and Clausen have found significantly lowered GSH-px activity in the erythrocytes from MS-patients (1977) and compared the prevalence of MS in the United States (Kurtzke 1975) with available statistics on the content of Se in forage crops (Kubota and Allaway 1972). As the latter only in part reflected the actual content of available Se in the human diet, the comparison could give nothing more than an indication of a possible correlation.

INTER-RELATIONSHIPS OF SELENIUM TO VITAMIN E AND TO OTHER TRACE ELEMENTS

Any hypothesis concerning the biochemical role of Se has to take into account the profound inter-relationship of Se to vitamin E.

A low vitamin E intake makes the dietary concentration of Se much more critical (Hoekstra 1974, Ullrey 1974), and it is well known that combinations of Se and vitamin E are sometimes required to cure animal disorders (Jansson et al. 1976, Judson and Obst 1975). The minimum requirement for Se may also vary with the nature of the rest of the diet, due to interactions between Se and other trace elements such as Hg, Cd, Pb, Zn, As and Mn (Lee 1975, Marjanen 1978). Thus it must be very difficult to establish by geographical comparisons only more than a broadly indicative correlation between known Se-deficient areas and the prevalence of MS in the world.

CORRELATIONS OF FOCI OF MULTIPLE SCLEROSIS AND SELENIUM-DEFICIENT AREAS

In some more limited national studies a close correlation has anyhow been found. Wikström and Palo have noted that the focal areas of MS in western Finland strikingly coincide with areas in which the cattle has been known to suffer from nutritional muscular dystrophy, a disorder caused by lack of Se and vitamin E (1976). They did also note that even if the role of these factors in the pathogenesis of MS is unknown, Se has a biochemical role as a component of GSH-px, which protects cell membranes from oxidative disintegration. It has also been noted that in Finland the highest Se values for blood serum were found in Lapps. among whom the prevalence of MS is low (Wikström—Westermarck—Palo 1976). Similarily it is possible to correlate MS-areas with Se-deficiency in Norway.

Prevalence rates per 100 000 population for probable MS in Europe pared to known areas of low availability of selenium[20]. Prevalence rates are shown with figures, and the darker the hatching the lesser the amounts of available Se in soils and crops. Some "white" countries on the map most probably have large areas that ought to be hatched – just as the hatched countries probably have some white spots (areas with enough Se in the soils). Our knowledge is at present limited.*
    Translation: Lägre MS-frekvens = Lower frequency of MS, Zon med hög MS-frekvens = Zone with high frequency of MS.

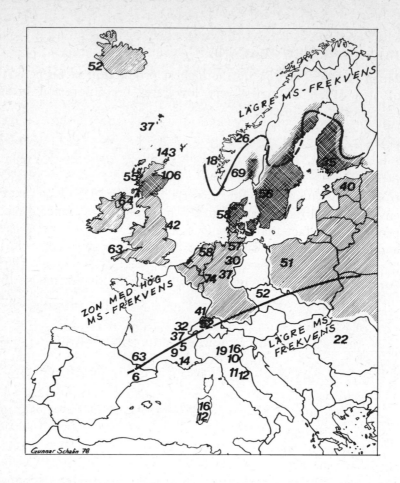

SELENIUM AND CANCER

Another strong argument supporting the hypothetical role of Se as the decisice factor in the latitudinal distribution of MS is the fact that the one and only disease with a similar world-wide distribution is cancer of the colon (Wolfgram 1975), a disease that has convincingly been shown to be related to lack of Se (Jansson et al. 1976). Even some other forms of cancer have been found to be inversely related to the amount of Se in the diet (Harr et al. 1973).

90

EFFECTS OF AVAILABILITY OF SELENIUM IN JAPAN AND NEW ZEALAND

Japan is characterized by the highest production of Se per unit of area of all countries, very low rates for colon and breast cancer (Jansson et al. 1976) and extremely low prevalence of MS (Kuroiwa 1977) — considering the high latitude of the country. In contrast New Zealand is characterized by a relatively high prevalence of MS (Hornabrook 1971) and very high rates for colon, rectum and breast cancer (Jansson et al. 1976). The two countries are situated on more or less the same latitudes and many environmental factors are similar. The decisive difference is most probably the fact that the soils of New Zealand in general have a rather low content of available Se and large areas deficient in Se, a fact well established (Wells 1966. Hartley and Grant 1961, Andrews et al. 1968) by the studies of the Se-responsive disorders afflicting the domestic animals in the country. The notable differences in dietary habits between the inhabitants of the two countries must also be of considerable importance. The Japanese eat much more fish, and the coastal waters around Japan are known to be richer in Se than most parts of the oceans (Lakin 1971) — and so are probably also many of the other different kinds of sea food the Japanese consume, as many sea-organisms are noted for a high ability to accumulate trace elements.

BIOLOGICALLY AVAILABLE SE IN SOILS AND PLANTS

The amount of biologically available Se is often quite different from what could be expected on the basis of analyses of the actual content of Se in soils and underlying bedrock. These should not be equated with the amounts available to plants, as many of the Se compounds are insoluble or otherwise unavailable. Different plant species have quite different ability to utilize different Se compounds, and even the soil type does affect the uptake of Se in many ways (Gissel-Nielsen 1976). The content of Se in one and the same plant also varies with the climatic conditions and during different stages of growth. Various parts of a plant may also contain varying amounts, and e.g. potato tubers grown in the same soil as swedes have been shown to contain only one tenth of the amount of Se in the latter (Bisbjerg 1972). Forage crops in general take up much more of the available Se than cereals, and it is thus quite possible that the local population can suffer from Se deficiency even in such areas where the pastures contain enough Se to prevent Se-responsive disorders among the cattle.

AGGRAVATING FACTORS IN INDUSTRIALIZED COUNTRIES

The more humid the area and the more acid the soil is, the greater the possibility of inadequacy of plant Se for animals (Johnson 1975). Our fossil fuels contain Se, which is volatilized during combustion, but probably in the form of insoluble oxides which do not increase the amount of available Se (Bolton et al. 1973, Johnson 1975), and the sulphur that is released at the same time has a negative influence. Sulphuric acid is formed in the atmosphere, and the rain that falls is making the soil more acid. The sulphates formed will negatively affect the vegetative uptake of chemically similar selenates from the soil (Bisbjerg 1972), especially badly in industrialized countries in higher latitudes that are already deficient in Se. Through manure considerable amounts of Se were formerly returned to the fields (Thomson 1972, Shamberger 1973) whereas the artificial fertilizers now in use generally contain only minute amounts of Se. Intensified farming practices also reduce the content of Se in soils. Irrigation increases leaching and volatile compounds escape from soils without vegetation cover through drying and rewetting (Gissel-Nielsen 1976). Selenium deficient crops are thus produced in the highly industrialized countries, especially in the more humid areas, where high yields are produced through intensive methods with liberal use of commercial fertilizers on strongly leached soils (Gissel-Nielsen 1976). The already serious problems in these Se deficient areas are thus aggravated. This may be the reason why the number of MS cases is increasing in some areas.

WEATHER AND CLIMATE AFFECT THE AVAILABILE AMOUNTS OF SELENIUM

Fluctuations in weather and climate conditions also affect the amount of available Se. In the Se-deficient areas in Finland an increase in the number of cases of muscular dystrophy among the cattle could be related to unusually cold and rainy periods in late summertime, which may have caused decreasing availability of Se (Lannek et al.) (cit. Bisbjerg 1972). In Australia rainy weather has been noted to decrease the amounts of available Se through waterlogging (Allaway 1972, Reuter 1975). In analogy it can be assumed that these phenomena also aggravates Se deficiency at higher latitudes with an excess of precipitation.

Seasonal variations also affect the availability of Se. During periods of rapid growth volatile Se compounds are lost through transpiration from the vegetative cover, and the plants do then contain less Se than normally (Reuter 1975). An increase has been noted during ripening (Gissel-Nielsen 1976) and from this it can be concluded that the time of harvesting also influences the Se content of crops. It is thus quite possible that ensilage fodder harvested before ripening will have an abnormally low content of Se, and that this may partly explain why Swedish meat does contain only minute amounts of Se compared with meat from other countries in Europe or the United States (Norrman 1977). Improved hybrid strains of fodder crops may also have reduced ability to utilize available Se, and Se intake may also differ between strains of animals (Judson and Obst 1975).

FARMING METHODS MAY REDUCE SE LEVELS IN SOIL

The question about how and in what amounts Se is leached during soil formation and in various farming practices can at present not be answered. Some experiments indicate that leaching is almost negligible in cultivated soil (Jones and Belling, op.cit) (Gissel-Nielsen 1976) but in this experiment the possible existence of a biological Se cycle was not accounted for. Increasing acidity of the soils does also increase the plant uptake of heavy metals (Christophersen 1975) such as cadmium and mercury that may reduce the availability of Se. Fertilizing with superphosphate has in experiments been noted to cause a decrease in Se concentrations in different plant species grown in pots (Gissel—Nielsen 1976), and high levels of sulphate in alfalfa has been found to reduce the availability of the Se content in the fodder, resulting in muscular dystrophy in calves that were fed this (Trace elements).

HUMAN INTAKE OF SELENIUM

The human intake of Se is mostly dependent on what our food contains. It is well known that drinking water in general plays a minor role as a source of trace elements to man compared with food (Hadjimarkos 1967). The dietary habits — kinds of food consumed, amounts consumed and frequency of consumption — are of utmost importance. Se deficiency is thus not primarily dependent on where people live but on what they eat. The influence of Se levels in the local soil must not be exaggerated.

SELENIUM IN OUR FOOD

The value of different foodstuffs as a source of Se depends on the form in which the element is present as well as on its concentration, at least for chicks and rats (Underwood 1975) but probably also for man. Plant sources generally have a much higher Se availability than animal products, but do often contain only minor amounts of Se. Seafoods, kidney, liver, meat and whole grains are generally good sources, but e.g. tuna Se is of low availability, possible caused by high content of mercury in tuna meat. Fruits and vegetables as well as potatoes are mostly poor sources of Se (Underwood 1975, Bisbjerg 1972). The Se content of human foods is further influenced by processing. Much of the Se in vegetables is normally discarded with the cooking water. Se is also lost in the refining of sugar. Considerably lower Se levels have been reported in white flour and bread than in whole wheat flour and bread. High contents of polyunsaturated fats in feed has been noted to increase the requirements of Se in domestic animals (Norrman 1977). The human consumption of various fats may also be of considerable importance. The correlation of fat consumpiton and increase of MS in Norway in the years after the second world war (Swank and Backer 1952) may thus be correct.

94

SELENIUM IN CEREALS AND IN HUMAN BLOOD

The cereals probably constitute the most important single source of Se for man. Analyses of the Se content in blood in the United States indicate that cereal products rich in Se normally supply enough to meet human requirements even in such areas where animals suffer from Se-responsive disorders and the meat does not contain enough Se. Only in such areas where locally grown cereals also contain only minor amounts, as in Sweden and on New Zealand, generally low contents of Se in human blood have been observed (Watkinson 1974). The cereals of Scandinavia are in general characterized by low Se levels (Lindberg et al. 1970, Gissel-Nielsen 1975) with a decreasing tendency. The apparently insufficient supply of Se through cereals is unfortunately not compensated through animal food products (apart from sea foods), as the domestic animals are fed locally grown fodder also lacking Se. Finland is in this respect an exception, as Se there has for more than 15 years been accepted as a feed additive to prevent Se-responsive disorders. In large parts of Canada the problem is the same as in Scandinavia. In West-Germany the natural content of Se is much higher, and the Se content of German meat and meat products is from twice up to four times higher than in corresponding Swedish products (Norrman 1977).

CONCLUSION

The minimum Se requirement of man varies with the form of Se ingested and the content in his food of elements with which Se interacts metabolically, just as it varies for our domestic animals (Underwood 1975, Gissel-Nielsen 1976). Thus not even the content of Se in our diet can be used as a measurement of how much biologically available Se it contains. It is quite impossible to draw a map that would in detail correlate the prevalence of MS with Se-deficient areas in the world, as neither the true prevalence of MS nor the actually available amounts of Se are really known. Surprisingly good correlation can however be noted in many countries. Further detailed studies of especially isolated rural areas may provide a better basis for conclusions about the relationship between the prevalence of MS and trace element deficiencies. At present it is only possible to draw the conclusion from the material available that the general availability of Se appears to be one of the decisive factors causing the focal and latitudinal distribution pattern of MS.

Literature

1. Acheson, E.D. 1961. Multiple sclerosis in British Commonwealth countries in the southern hemisphere. In:Brit. J. prev. soc. med., 15, 118.
2. Ackermann, A. 1931. Die multiple Sklerose in der Schweiz. In: Schweiz. med.Wschr., 61, 1245–1250.
3. Allaway, W.H., H.A. Laitinen, H.W. Lakin, and O.H. Muth 1974. Selenium. In: Geochemistry and the environment, vol I: The relation of selected trace elements to health and disease, Nat.Acad.o.Sc., Wash.DC.
4. Alter, M., R.S. Allison, O.R. Talbert and L.T. Kurland. 1960. Geographic distribution of multiple sclerosis, comparison of prevalence in Charleston county, South Carolina, USA and Halifax county, Nova Scotia, Canada. In:Wld. Neurol., 1, 55.
5. Alter, M., U. Leibowitz and J. Speer. 1966. Risk of multiple sclerosis related to age at immigration to Israel. In: Arch. Neurol. (Chic.), 15, 234–237.
6. Alter M., M. Yamoor, and M. Harshe. 1974. Multiple sclerosis and nutrition. In. Arch. Neurol. 31. Oct. 1974.
7. Andrews, E.D., W.J. Hartley and A.B. Grant, 1968: Selenium-responsive diseases of animals in New Zealand. In: New Zealand veterinary journal, 16, 3–17.
8. Barlow, G.S. 1960. Correlation of geographic distribution of multiple sclrosis with cosmic-ray intensities. In: Acta psychiat.scand. (supp. 147) 35, 108.
9. Bing, R. and H. Reese. 1926. Die multiple Sklerose in der Nordwest-schweiz. In: Schweiz.med.Wschr., 56, 30–34.
10. Bird, Allan V., and Eijiro Satyoshi. 1975. Comparative epidemiological studies of multiple sclerosis in South Africa and Japan. In: Journal of neurology, neurosurgery and psychiatry, 1975, 38, 911–918.
11. Bisbjerg, Birte. 1972. Studies on Selenium in plants and soils. Risø Report, No. 200 from: Danish Atomic Energy Commission Research Establishment Risø.
12. Bolton, N.E. et al. 1973. Trace element measurments at the Coal-Fired Allen Stream Plant. Progress report, June 1971–January 1973. ORNL-NSF-EP-43, Oak Ridge National Laboratory. Oak Ridge, Tenn.
13. Campbell, A.M.G., P. Daniel, R.J. Porter, W.R. Russel, H.V. Smith and J.R.M. Innes. 1974. Disease of the nervous system occuring among research workers on swayback in lambs. In: Brain, 80:50–58.
14. Christophersen, Olav Albert. 1975. Betydningen av krom og selen i kostholdet. Manuscript dated Oslo 31–5–1975.

96

15. Dean, G., and J.F. Kurtzke. 1971. On the risk of multiple sclerosis according to age at immigration to South Africa. In: Br. Med.J. 2(1971), 724–730.

16. Detels, R , B. Visscher, A. Coulson, R. Malmgren and J. Dudley. 1976. Relationship of environment, ethnicity and migration to multiple sclerosis. In. Neurology, 26 (1976), 6 Abstract No. 2.

17. Diplock, A.T. 1973. A possible inter-relationship between selenium toxicity and the biochemical function of trace amounts of selenium. In: Trace substances in environmental health. VII, University of Missouri 1973.

18. Gardiner and Gorman. 1963. The relation between Se content of plants and mean annual rainfall. In: Australian journal of experimental agriculture and animal husbandry, reprinted in Trace elements in soil-plant-animal systems p. 293.

19. Georgi, F. and P. Hall. 1960. Studies on multiple sclerosis frequency in Switzerland and East Africa. In: Acta psychiat. scand. suppl. 147, 75–84.

20. Gissel-Nielsen, Gunnar. 1976. Selenium in soils and plants. Unpubl. report from Agricultural Research Department Research Establishment Risø Roskilde, Danmark.

21. Godwin, K.O. 1975. The role and the metabolism of selenium in the animal. In: Trace elements in soil-plant-animal-systems.

22. Gordon, G.E. et al. 1973. Abnormally enriched trace elements in the atmosphere. In. Trace substances in environmental health, VII. University of Missouri 1973.

23. Greenham. L.W., and D.B. Peacock. 1975. Geographical distribution of multiple sclerosis. In: The Lancet, Jan. 11., 1975.

24. Hadjimarkos, D.M. 1967. Effect of trace elements in drinking water on dental caries J. Pediatr. 70, 967–69.

25. – (1973) Trace elements and dental health. In: Trace substances in environmental health, VII, Missouri 1973.

26. Harr, J.R., J.H. Exon, P.H. Weswig and Whanger, P.D. 1973. Relationship of dietary selenium concentration, chemical cancer induction and tissue concentration of selenium in rats. In: Clinical toxicology, 6(3), 487–495.

27. Hartley, W.J., and A.B. Grant. 1961. A review of selenium responsive diseases of New Zealand livestock. In: Federation proceedings, 20, 679–688.

28. Hemphill, Delbert D. (ed.). 1973. Trace substances in environmental health. Procedings of University of Missouri's 7th Annual Conference on trace substances in environmental health, 1973.

29. Hoekstra, William G. 1974. Biochemical role of selenium. In: Trace element metabolism in animals, 2.

30. Hornabrook, R.W. 1971. The prevalence of multiple sclerosis in New Zealand. In: Acta neurol. Scand. 47, 1971. 426–438.
31. Hyllested, K. 1956. Disseminated sclerosis in Denmark, prevalence and geographical distribution. Copenhagen 1956.
32. Jansson, B., M.A. Malahy and G.B. Seibert. 1976. Geographical distribution of gastrointestinal cancer and breast cancer and its relation to selenium deficiency. From: National large bowel cancer project. The Univerisity of Texas System Cancer Center MD Anderson Hospital and Tumor Institute, Houston, Texas.
33. Johnson, C.M. 1975. Selenium in soils and plants: Contrasts in conditions providing safe but adequate amounts of selenium in food chains. In: Trace elements in soil-plant-animal systems.
34. Judson, G.J., and J.M. Obst. 1975. Diagnosis and treatment of selenium inadequacies in the grazing ruminant. In: Trace elements in soil-plant-animal systems.
35. Kubota, J., and W.H. Allaway. 1972. Micronutrients in agriculture.
36. Kurland, L.T., M. Alter, and P. Bailey. 1957. Geomedical and other epidemiological considerations on multiple sclerosis. In: Vol. 1, Int. Neurol. Congr. Brussels, 1957, p. 11.
37. Kurland, L.T., and K.B. Westlund. 1954. Epidemiologic factors in the etiology and prognosis of multiple sclerosis. In: Ann.NY Acad.Sci., 58, 682.
38. Kuroiwa, Y., T-P. Hung, D. Landsborough, C.S. Park, B.S. Singhal, S. Soemargo, A. Vejjajiva, and H. Shibasaki. 1977. Multiple sclerosis in Asia. In: Neurology, Feb. 1977. 188–192.
39. Kuroiwa, Y., A. Igata, K. Itahara, S. Koshijima, T. Tsubaki, Y. Toyokura and H. Shibasaki. 1975. Nationwide survey of multiple sclerosis in Japan. In: Neurology, 25, 845–851, Sept. 1975, 845–851.
40. Kuroiwa, Yoshigoro, and Hiroshi Shibasaki. 1976. Epidemiologic and clinical studies of multiple sclerosis in Japan. In: Neurology, June 1976, Part 2.
41. Kurtzke, John F. 1965. Familial incidence and geography in multiple sclerosis. In: Acta neurol.Scand., 41, 127–139.
42. – 1966. An eveluation of the geographic distribution of multiple sclerosis. In: Acta neurol. Scand., 41 (1966), Suppl. 19, 91–177.
43. – 1967. Further considerations on the geographic distribution of multiple sclerosis. In: Acta neurol. Scand., 43, 283–298.
44. – 1974. Further features of the Fennoscandian focus of multiple sclerosis. In: Acta neurol. Scand., 50, 478–502.
45. – 1975. A reassessment of the distribution of multiple sclerosis. In: Acta neurol. Scand., 51, 110–136.
46. Kurtzke, Johan F., and Kay Hyllested. 1975. Multiple sclerosis: An epide-

mic disease in the Faeroes. In: Transactions of the American Neurological Association, 1975, 213–215.

47. Lakin, H.W. 1961. Geochemistry of selenium in relation to agriculture. In: Selenium in agriculture, US Dep. of Agriculture, Agricultural Handbook, No. 200.

48. Layton, W., and J.M. Sutherland. 1975. Geochemistry and multiple schlerosis: A hypothesis. In: Med.J.Austr., 1975:1, 73–77.

49. Lee, H.J.. 1975. Trace elements in animal production. In: Trace elements in soil-plant-animal systems.

50. Leibowitz, U. 1970. Multiple sclerosis: Progress in epidemiologic and experimental research. In: Journal of the neurological sciences, 1971. 12, 307–318.

51. Liljequist, Gösta. 1962. Meteorologi.

52. Lindberg, Paul and Sven Bingefors. 1970. Selenium levels of forages and soils in different regions of Sweden. In: Acta agr. Scand., 20.

53. Låg, J., and E. Steinnes. 1974. Soil selenium in relation to precipitation. In: Ambio, 3, No. 6, 1974.

54. – 1978. Regional distribution of selenium and arsenic in humus layers of Norwegian forest soils. In: Geoderma, 20. 1978.

55. Mc Alpine, D., N.D. Compston, and C.E. Lumsden. 1955. Multiple sclerosis. Edinburgh and London 1955.

56. McCall, M.G., T.Le G. Brereton, A. Dawson, K. Millingen, J.M. Sutherland, and E.D. Acheson. 1968. Frequency of multiple sclerosis in three Australian cities – Perth, Newcastle and Hobart. In: J. Neurosurg. Psychiat., 1968, 31, 1–9.

57. Macchi, G., M. Saginario, and S. Valla. 1962. La sclérose en plaques dans le province de Parme (Italie). In: World Neurology, 3, 1962. 731–9.

58. Marjanen, Helvi and Sylvi Soini. 1978. Kivennäisaineiden ja vitamiinien merkityksestä. Helsinki 1978.

59. Metropolitan Life Statistical Bulletin, March 1975, 2–5.

60. Morris, VC, and O.A. Levander. 1970. Selenium content of foods. In: Journal of Nutrition, 100, 1383–1388.

61. Murray, I.J. 1976. An unusual occurrence of multiple sclerosis in a small rural community. In: Journal canadien des sciences neurologiques, 3, No. 3, 163–166.

62. Norrish, K. 1975. Geochemistry and mineralogy of trace elements. In: Trace elements in soil-plant-animal-systems.

63. Norrman, Eric. 1977. Selebrist. In: Vår Näring, 2/1977.

64. – 1977. Husdjurens behov av selen. Unpubl. material from Lantbrukshögskolan, Konsulentavd/husdjur, Uppsala.

65. Olson, O.E. 1967. Selenium in biomedicine, Cycling of Se in nature. Repr. in: Trace elements in soil-plant-animal systems, 1975.

66. Ottesen, Rolf Tore. Sammenstilling av data over metallinnhold i norsk jord med henblikk på sykdomsfrekvens. Multiple sclerose — bly. Unpublished report 1494A from Norges geologiske undersøkelse.
67. — 1977. Sammenstilling av geokjemiske og medisinske data i Norge. Unpublished report 1494C from Norges geologiske undersøkelse.
68. Palo, J., J. Wikström, and E. Kivalo. 1973. Epidemiology of nutritional muscular dystrophy and multiple sclerosis. In: The Lancet, Oct. 13, 1973.
69. Pålsson, P.A., I.H. Pattison, and E.J. Field. Transmission experiments with multiple sclerosis. In: NINDB Monograph, No. 2, "Slow, latent and temperate virus infections", pp. 49—54.
70. Pettersson, Olle. 1976. Tungmetaller i mark och växter. En litteraturöversikt. Uppsala 1976.
71. Poskanzer, D., K. Schapira, and H. Millar. 1963. Multiple sclerosis and poliomyelitis. In: The Lancet, 2 (1963), 917—921.
72. Poskanzer, D., A. Walker, J. Yonkondy, and J. Sheridan. 1976. Studies in the epidemiology of multiple sclerosis in the Orkney and Shetland Islands. In: Neurology, June 1976, Part 2, Abstract 4.
73. Reuter, D.J. 1975. The recognition and correction of trace element deficiencies. In: Trace elements in soil-plant-animal systems.
74. Rinne, U.K., M. Panelius, E. Kivalo, E. Hokkanen, and J. Palo. 1966. Distribution of multiple sclerosis in Finland, with special reference to some geological factors. In: Acta neurol. Scand., 42, 385—399.
75. Salmi, Martti. 1963. On relations between geology and multiple sclerosis. In: Acta geographica, 17, No. 4.
76. Satoyoshi, E., A. Saku, N. Sunohara, and M. Kinoshita. 1976. Clinical manifestations and the diagnostic problems of multiple sclerosis in Japan. In: Neurology, 26 (1976), 6, part 2, Abstract No. 7.
77. Shamberger, Raymond J. et al. 1973. Antioxidants and cancer. Selenium distribution and human cancer mortality in the United States, Canada and New Zealand. In: Trace substances in environmental health, VII, University of Missouri 1973.
78. Shatin, R. 1964. Multiple sclerosis and geography. In: Neurology, 14, 338—344.
79. Shukla, V.K.S., G.E. Jensen, and J. Clausen. 1977. Erythrocyte glutathione peroxidase deficiency in multiple sclerosis. In: Acta neurol. Scand. 56, 542—550.
80. Siedler, H., W. Nicholl, L. Kurland. 1958. The prevalence and incidence of multiple sclerosis in Missoula County, Montana. In: The Journal-Lancet, 78, 358—360.
81. Spillane, J.D. 1972. The geography of neurology. In: British Medical journal, 1972, 2, 506—512.

82. Sutherland, John M., John H. Tyrer, and Mervyn J. Eadie. 1962. The prevalence of multiple sclerosis in Australia. In: Brain, 85, 149–164.
83. Swank, R., and Julie Backer. 1950. The geographic incidence of multiple sclerosis in Norway. In: Transactions Amer.Neurol. Ass., 75 (1950), 274–275.
84. Swank, R., O. Lerstad, A. Strøm, and J. Backer. 1952. Multiple sclerosis in rural Norway. In: The New England Journal of Medicine, 246, 19, 721–728.
85. Teppo, L., M. Hakama, T. Hakulinen, M. Lehtonen, and E. Saxén. 1975. Cancer in Finland 1953–1970: Incidence, mortality, prevalence. In: Acta pathologica et microbiologica Scandinavia, Section A, Suppl. No. 252.
86. Trace element metabolism in animals, 2. Ed. by W.G. Hoekstra et al. International symposium in Madison, Wis., 1973. Baltimore 1974.
87. Trace elements in soil-plant-animal-system. Ed. by D.J.D. Nicholas and Adrian R. Egan. University of Adelaide, Waite agricultural research institute. Jubilee symposium 1974. London 1975.
88. Ullrey, Duane E. 1974. The selenium-deficiency problem in animal agriculture. In: Trace element metabolism in animals, 2.
89. Underwood, E.J. 1975. Trace elements and their physiological roles in the animal. In: Trace elements in soil-plant-animal systems.
90. Watkinson, J.H. 1974. The selenium status of New Zealanders. In: New Zealand Med. J., Sept. 11, 1974, 202–205.
91. Wells, N. 1966. Selenium in horizons of soil profiles. In: New Zealand Journal of Science, 10, 142–179, March 1967.
92. Westlund, K. 1970. Distribution and mortality time trend of multiple sclerosis and some other diseases in Norway. In: Acta neurol. Scand., 46 (1970).
93. Westlund, Knut B., and, Leonard T. Kurland. 1952. Studies on multiple sclerosis in Winnipeg, Manitoba and New Orleans, Louisiana. In: Am.J.Hyg., 1953. 57, 397–407.
94. Wikström, Juhani. 1975. The epidemiology of optic neuritis in Finland and The epidemiology of multiple sclerosis and tuberculosis in Finland. In: Acta neurol. Scand., 52, 196–206.
95. Wikström, Juhani, and Jorma Palo. 1975. Studies on the clustering of multiple sclerosis in Finland I: Comparison between the domeciles and places of birth in selected subpopulations. In: Acta neurol. Scand., 51, 85–98.
96. – 1976. Studies on the geographic clustering of multiple sclerosis and optic neuritis in Finland. In: J.Neurol., 213, 79–85 (1976).
97. Wikström, J., T. Westermarck, and J. Palo. 1976. Selenium, vitamine E and copper in multiple sclerosis. In: Acta neurol. Scand., 54, 287–290.

98. Wolfgang, Frederick. 1975. Similar geographical distribution of multiple sclerosis and cancer of the colon. In: Acta neurol. Scand., 52, 294–302.

A Hypothesis Concerning Multiple Schlerosis and its Possible Connection with Disturbed Fat Metabolism in Selenium Deficiency

Britt Ahlrot-Westerlund

A new hypothesis on the role of the selenoenzyme GSH-px, in particular, and of vitamin E in the pathogensis of MS is discussed. GSH-px is considered to be a first range defender of cell membranes against lipid peroxidation.

MS seems to develop against a background of disturbed fat metabolism. Some hypothetical consequences of damage to various cell membranes are discussed. Further research and possible treatment are suggested.

Multiple sclerosis, MS, is presumably caused by a combination of several factors. Besides a contagious agent (or agents) of the slow virus type, so far not identified, a disturbed fat metabolism seems to be of importance (1) and to affect certain cell membranes (1,2). This disturbance may be a consequence of subnormal activity of the enzyme glutathion peroxydase (GSH-px), which needs selenium for its function.

EVIDENCE IN FAVOUR OF THE GLUTATHION PEROXIDAS HYPOTHESIS

Structure and function of GSH-px and vitamin E (short introduction)

GSH-px seems to be present in all cells of the body in variable amounts, as well as glutathion, the matrix of the enzyme (3,4). Its natural substrates are e.g. steroids, DNA, fatty acids, and H_2O_2.

GSH-px inhibits the loss of unsaturated fatty acids from cell membranes, and vitamin E (α-tocopherol) prevents formation of organic peroxides, thus safeguarding cell membranes against attacks on their polyunsaturated membrane lipids by free radicals (3-8) formed from peroxides during the metabolism of unsaturated fatty acids. The chemical structure of GSH-px is not yet known. However, it is known that each enzyme molecule contains four selenium atoms (4, 5).

GSH-px seems to cooperate with vitamin E in its control of peroxide levels in the body. The precise mode of action has not been clarified, but the vitamin seems to prevent formation of peroxides, while the enzyme decomposes them. The two reactions can only to a limited extent replace each other (4, 8, 9, 10).

GSH-px, Selenium and vitamin E in MS

It has been observed that subnormal GSH-px activity results in a damage to cell membranes (4, 5, 6, 8). This seems to be essential in the MS pathogenesis. Cells rich in phospholipids may be expected to be more susceptible than others to damage at GSH-px deficiancy or at low enzyme activity.

As already stated, GSH-px needs selenium for its activity. The necessity of selenium intake with food is well documented in animals, and there is reason to believe that this also applies to man; though no dramatic effects are seen in selenium deficiency, it may have long-term effects on health (3, 4, 11, 12). MS has been shown to occur more frequently in areas with low concentrations of selenium available to plants. This is particularly obvious in isolated areas where most of the food consumed is produced locally (13-19). Moreover, Shukla et al. (20) demonstrated a significantly lowered GSH-px activity in 24 MS-patients, as compared to controls.

Further evidence of the role of GSH-px activity and selenium concentration is based on observations on animals. Veterinaries have long been aware of the need for sufficient GSH-px activity and for supply of vitamin E in animals during fast growth, i.e. fast cell division (3, 4, 5, 10, 16, 21).

From these considerations it is proposed that availability of sufficient selenium and vitamin E during adolescence may thus be crucial factors in the prevention of MS.

104

Erythrocyte membrane lipids in MS-patients

Erythrocytes show the second highest concentration of phospholipids in cell membranes of the body. It has been found that erythrocytes from MS-patients have a slightly increased mean diameter. This finding points to altered osmotic membrane properties. These erythrocytes also show increased fragility (2). These observations may be explained by changes in the chemical properties of the membrane phospholipids, caused by subnormal GSH-px activity, due to Se-deficiency (22, 23).

Some evidence in favour of this aspect was given by Field et al. (24). Using the erythrocyte-mobility test (24) these authors found a lower mobility in erythrocytes from MS-patients as compared with those from controls. This fact was related to the low concentration of unsaturated fatty acids observed in serum from MS-patients (1, 2, 24, 25). A moderate abnormality in the erythrocyte-mobility test has also been found in 40% of relatives, particulary mothers, of MS-patients (24). No attempts to correlate these findings with a subnormal GSH-px activity have been made before. Instead, the observations have simply been explained as a matter of heredity. Subnormal GSH-px activity as such may, however, be caused by hereditary factors. A prevalence of MS in the females may also point to hereditary factors, but could also be explained by correlation between sex hormones and GSH-px activity, as the enzyme is involved in the steroid metabolism. On the other hand, dietary factors may be of importance, too.

Serum unsaturated fatty acids in MS-patients

Subnormal concentrations of unsaturated fatty acids have been found in serum from MS-patients (2,26,27). This has been explained by an assumed high intake of saturated fatty acids in the food, as there is a high frequency of MS in regions where a diet rich in fat is usual. The last mentioned explanation is, however, contradicted by observations of Callaghan et al. (28). These authors made an investigation comprising 102 persons: 51 MS-patients at various stages of the disease, 31 cases suffering from other neurological diseases also at various stages, and 20 controls. Their food was controlled for one week and analyzed for calories, proteins, carbohydrates, and fat. The consumption of linolenic acid was expressed as a percentage of the total amount of fat in the food. No significant difference was found in the intake of unsaturated fatty acids in the three groups. Furthermore, Belin et al. (27) showed that the absorption by the digestive tract of linolenic acid was normal in MS-patients. Consequently, the findings of low concentrations of unsaturated fatty acids in serum from MS-patients do not seem to be caused by differences in diet or absorption.

Very much simplified: Synthesis and oxidative decomposition of unsaturated fatty acids take place in the membranes surrounding liver microsomes and mitochondria (21, 29, 30, 31). Transportation of fatty acids across those cell membranes may include their incorporation into phospholipids (32-34).

The GSH-px activity in liver microsomes and mitochondria is normally high compared with other tissues. Assuming that the GSH-px activity in MS-patients is generally decreased, a disturbance in the synthesis as well as the decomposition and transportation of unsaturated fatty acids across cell membranes is likely to occur. In that case, the risk for abnormal peroxidation effects would increase (35-38), thus decreasing the amount of unsaturated fatty acids in serum. It may be possible to study this hypothesis by analysis of liver tissue in man for GSH-px activity, obtained by biopsy.

The following observation is of particular interest in this context. The linoleate ester fraction in serum decreases shortly before or simultaneously with acute clinical detoriation of MS (26). A plausible explanation would seem to be that under the influence of low GSH-px activity, lipid peroxides accumulate in liver microsomes and mitochondria, causing an acute decrease in unsaturated fatty acids.

In summary: sufficient selenium supply maintains GSH-px activity in liver microsomes and mitochondria and normal metabolism of unsaturated fatty acids. Lack of selenium and consequently decreased GSH-px activity, on the other hand, lead to membrane damage and disturbed unsaturated fatty acids metabolism and transport. With this background contradictory observations on plasma linoleate levels and erythrocyte-mobility tests may be comprehensible (39-41).

106

CNS cells and T-lymphocytes in MS

The cells of the central nervous system (CNS) and the T-lymphocytes are so called GO-cells (unable to form new cells by division). They are therefore vulnerable. The oligodendroglia cells belong to this kind of cells. Their cytoplasm forms the myelin and constitutes the most phospholipidrich material in the body.

Some unsaturated fatty acids are essential components in phospholipids of the cell membranes, e.g. α-linolenic acid, linolenic acid, and arachidonic acid. If polyunsaturated fatty acids are not available in sufficient amounts for the myelinization process (which extends to about 16 years of age) either because of insufficient supply or a disturbed metabolism (e.g. in selenium deficiency), the result may become a myelin with subnormal stability, vulnerable· to, inter alia, peroxidation processes (42, 43). Breakdown of the myelin would also release parts of the basic protein, constituting 40% of myelin sheath. This basic protein, also called encephalitogenic factor (E.F.), might be bound to T-lymphocytes and thus become antigenic (44, 45). The sensitized T-lymphocytes seem to be an essential cause of the autoimmune reaction in CNS and destruction of myelin. The phospholipid membranes of the lymphocytes are supposed to be damaged too (46, 47).

Lymphocyte membrane. Scrapie

It is an open question whether or not injured lymphocyte membranes (46, 47) are more easily affected by various contagious matters, e.g. a virus or a virus-genom, in a preclinical stage of MS. In scrapie, a neurological sheep desease, a still not identified contagious agent is found in cell membranes. Scrapie and MS have several similar characteristics, inter alia, no antibodies or interferon are formed. In MS, however, interferon may have been formed in a preclinical stage long before the first indications of an autoimmune reaction in CNS appear (48-55).

Autoimmune reactions and antibodies in MS

Some further comments on the lymphocytes at MS seem to be of interest. Field, Caspary & Madgwich (56) showed in 1972

107

that sensitization of guinea pigs to measles is accompanied by sensitization to encephalitogenic factors, E.F. Moreover, guinea pigs injected with E.F. develop some degree of lymphocyte sensitization to measles, leading to an increased antibody titer to measles reflected in the cerebral liquor. Consequently injured brain tissue shares its determinants with measles antigen, resulting in an increased titer of antibodies to measles virus. These circumstances seem to be analogous to the pathological course of MS.

In 1973 Field & McDermott (57) repeated the experiments mentioned above, using a different method, and found that E.F., and to a less extent measles antigen (or measles vaccin), are fixed to lymphocytes sensitized to E.F. in patients with measles or individuals treated with measles vaccin. The authors conclude that measles and E.F. cross-react, thus confirming the results of 1972 mentioned above (56).

An interesting question seems to be wether the ability of MS-lymphocytes to cross-react may indicate an injury in cell membranes which has contributed to altered immunological conditions (58).

Norrby & Vandvik (59) abserved that in MS only a minor fraction of the total oligoclonal IgG of the cerebrospinal fluid can be shown to represent measles-specific antibodies. However, measles antigen reularly removes the oligoclonal bands from the cerebrospinal fluid from patients with subacute sclerosing panencephalitis (59,60).

Platelets aggregation and Prostaglandins in MS

The platelets show a slight tendency of aggregation in MS. This phenomenon has been correlated to peroxidized fatty acids on the surface of the platelets (2, 61).

When any perturbance affects the cell membrane, arachidonic acid seems to be released. The acid is then rapidly metabolized into oxidized products, among them stable prostaglandins (62). Nugteren & Hazelhof (63) found that GSH-px is possibly one of the enzymes involved in the synthesis of prostaglandin (i.e. the step between the prostaglandin peroxides: $PGG_2 \rightarrow PGH_2$). In 1975 Srivastava et al. (64) demonstrated that the platelets from MS-patients have a reduced ability to synthesize prost-aglandins.

Although the augmented platelet aggregation does not seem to cause an increased tendency to peripheral thrombosis in MS-patients, it may cause microinfarcts in the postcapillary venules of the brain, and thus contribute to the formation of plaques (1).

Future reaearch

In order to test the hypothetical role of selenium and GSH-px in MS the following investigations are suggested in MS-patients and controls:
- GSH-px activity in blood cells, in particular erythrocytes and thrombocytes
- GSH-px activity in close relatives of MS-patients.
- Concentration of unsaturated fatty acids in serum compared with the GSH-px activity (Diet to be recorded).
- Possible variation with age and sex of GSH-px activity in series of about ten boys and girls of each age group.
- GSH-px activity in microsomes and mitochondria in liver biop-sies from MS-patients, especially cases with low concentrations of unsaturated fatty acids in serum, as well as with low GSH-px activity in erythrocytes. However, for ethical reasons, this in-vestigation is not likely to be feasible.
- Urinary excretion of selenium.
- Erythrocyte-mobility test in selenium-depleted animals, e.g. rats.

If the hypothesis is proved to be correct, it points to a way of treating MS. The purpose of such a treatment should be a stabili-zation of the cell membranes (cf. the effect of steroids and ACTH) and a cessation of the autoimmune response from E.F.-sensitized lymphocytes in CNS, thus
- Administration of selenium (possibly also vitamin E). The GSH-px activity to be checked during the course of treat-ment.
- Removal of sensitized lymphocytes from the circulating blood, e.g. by adsorption in a closed extracorporeal circuit.

However, no method seems to be presently available.

Finally, a comment on the frequently recommended treatment of MS by adding unsaturated fatty acids to the diet. The absorption seems to be normal, and the disturbance is probably located to the liver microsomes and mitochondria. Consequently, normalization of a sub-normal GSH-px activity by the treatment suggested above would seem to be prerequisite for therapeutic result.

Addendum. So far I have had the opportunity to investigate only one MS-patient for GSH-px activity: a 25-year-old female with confirmed diagnosis. She has had two relapses, the last one more than two years ago. Presently she seems to be in a healthy state with a good appetite, and she is able to work full day. She had a very low GSH-px activity as compared with the standard of the laboratory (one-third of the lower normal value). She was treated per os with 50 μg per day of an organic selenium compound. At re-examination two months later her GSH-px activity was increased by more than a factor of two. A third investigation (double test) was carried out three months later. For the last two months she had been supplied with only 25 μg per day of the selenium compound. The GSH-px activity was then found to be normal.

REFERENCES

1. Hubert S. Mickel: Multiple sclerosis. A new hypothesis. Perspectives in biology and medicine, 18, 1975, p.363-374.
2. S. Gul et al.: Fatty acid composition of phospholipids from platelets and erythrocytes in multiple sclerosis. N. Neurol. Neurosurg. Psychiat. 33, 1970, p.506-510.
3. Underwood: Selenium. Trace elements in human and animal nutrition, 1977,p.302-340.
4. W.G. Hoekstra: Biochemical role of selenium. Int. Symp. on trace elements metabolism in animals, 2, 1973,p.61-77.
5. Leopold Flohé et al.: Glutathione-peroxidase. Glutathionemetabolism and function, 1976 (ed. by Irwin Arias and William J.Jacoby), p.115-135.
6. Paul B.McCay et al.: Effect of glutathione-peroxidase activity on lipid peroxidation in biological membranes. Biochim. Biophys. Acta (Amst.) 431, 1976,p.459-468.

7. J.Green: Vitamin E and the biological antioxidant theory. Ann. N.Y. Acad. sci, 203, 1972,p.29-44.
8. N.Y. Jack Yang et al.: Vitamin E supplementation and glutathione peroxidase activity. Proc. Soc. exp. Biol. Med. (N.Y.), 151, 1976, p. 770-774.
9. Hiryuki Shimasaki and O.S.Privett: Studies on the role of vitamin E in the oxidation of blood components by fatty hydroperoxides. Arch. Biochem. Biophys. 169, 1975, p. 506-512.
10. P.J. Smith et al.: Glutathione peroxidase activity as a function of dietary selenomethionine. Nature, 247, 1974,p.392-393.
11. Birger Janson et al.: Geographical distribution of gastrointestinal cancer and breastcancer and its relation to selenium deficiency. Proc. Int. Symp. Detection and Prevention of Cancer, New York, 1976.
12. F. Wolfgram: Similar geographical distribution of multiple sclerosis and cancer of the colon. Acta Neurol. Scand., 52, 1975,p.294-302.
13. Nora M. Griffith, Christine D. Thomson: Selenium in whole blood of New Zealand residents. N.Z. med. J. 80, 1974, p.199-202.
14. J.H. Watkinson: The selenium status of New Zealanders. N.Z. 80, 1974,p.202.
15. Erik Norrman: Husdjurens behov av selen. Lantbrukshögskolan, May 11th, 1977, stencil.
16. Nils Lannek and Paul Lindberg: Vitamin E and selenium deficiencies of domestic animals. Advanc vet Sci. comp. med., vol. 19, 1975,p.127-163.
17. W.J. Harley and A.B. Grant: A review of selenium responsive diseases of New Zealand livestock. Fed. Proc. 20 (1961), 2.p.679-688.
18. Gunnar Schalin: A review of the world-wide occurence of multiple sclerosis and possible factors that might explain the geographical distribution of the disease, such as variations in the amount of available selen. Symposium om geomedisinske problemer, Oslo, May 22-23, 1978.
19. G.J. Judson and J.M. Obst: Diagnosis and treatment of selenium inadequacies in the grazing ruminant. Trace elements in human and animal nutrition, 1975,p.385-401.
20. V.K.S. Shukla, Gunde Egeskov and Jørgen Clausen: Erythrocyte glutathione peroxidase deficiency in multiple sclerosis. Acta Neurol. Scand., 56, 1977,p.542-550.
21. Lynn S. Grinna: Effect of dietary α-tecopherol on liver microsomes and mitochondria of aging rats. J.Nutr. 106, 1976,p.918-929.
22. Tuomas Westermarck and Markus Sandholm: Decreased erythrocyte glutathione peroxidase activity in neuroronal ceroid lipofuscinosis - corrected with selenium supplementation. Acta pharmacol. et. toxicol., 1977, 40,p.70-74.

23. W.M. Allen et al.: Selenium and the activity of glutathione peroxidase in bovine erythrocytes. The Veterinary Record, April 19, 1975,p.360.
24. E.J. Field et al.: Erythrocyte-mobility test for multiple sclerosis: Implications for pathogenesis and handling of the disease. J.Neurol., 214, 1977,p.113-127.
25. H. Meyer-Rienecker et al.: Der Makrophagen-Elektrophorese Mobilitäts-LAD-Test als diagnostisches Verfahren fur die multiple Sklerose. J.Neurol., 211 (1976),p.229-240.
26. R.W.R. Baker et al.: Serum cholestrol linoleate levels in multiple sclerosis, J.Neurol. Neurosurg. Psychiat. 28 (1965), p. 212-217.
27. J. Belin et al.: Linoleate metabolism in multiple sclerosis. J.Neurol. Neurosurg. Psychiat., 34, 1971,p.25-29.
28. Noel Callaghan et al.: Dietary intake of linoleic acid in multiple sclerosis and other diseases. J.Neurol. Neurosurg. Psychiat., 1973, 36,p.668-673.
29. Jagannath G. Satav et al.: Further characterization of rat liver mito-chondrial fractions. Lipid composition and synthesis and protein profiles. Biochem. J.(1976), 156,p.215-223.
30. C. Landriscina et al.: Turnover of fatty acids in rat liver cardiolipin: Comparison with other mitochondrial phospholipids. Lipids, Jan. 1976, 11, N:o 1,p.61-66.
31. Natalia Lopez-Moratalla et al.: Phospholipidperoxidation and release of cytochromes from inner mitochondrial membranes. Rev. esp. Fisiol. 31, 1975,p.215-222.
32. Masako Taniguchi and Toshio Sakagami: Exchange of phospohilipids between rough and smooth microsomes in vitro. J.Biochem., 77, 1975,p.1245-1248.
33. Karl Y. Hostetler et al.: Abnormal membrane phospholipid content in subcellular fractions from the morris 7777 hepatoma. Biochim. biophys. Acta.(Amst.), 441, 1976,p.231-238.
34. Willem Renooij et al.: Topological assymmetry of phospholipid meta-bolism in rat erythrocyte membranes. Evidence for flip-flop of lecithin. Europ. J.Biochem., 6, 1976,p.53-58.
35. Anonymus: Lipid peroxidation and GSH-px in the liver of cholester-olfed rats. Exp. Nutrition, 34, No. 2, Febr. 1976.
36. Sydney O. Alozie et al.: Effects of vitamin E-deficiency on GSH-induced swelling of rat liver mitochondria. Proc. Soc. exp. Biol. Med. (N.Y.) 148 (1975),p.929-932.
37. Nozamu Oshino and Britton Chance: Properties of glutathione release observed during reduction of organic hydroperoxide, demethylation of aminopyrine and oxidation of some substances in perfused rat liver, and their implications for the physiological function of catalase. Biochem. J.162 (1977), p.509-525.

38. Katsuyuki Nishiki et al.: Oxygen toxicity in the perfused rat liver and lung under hyperbaric conditions. Biochem. J., 160 (1976),p.343-355.
39. R.Heipertz et al.: Serum fatty acids in multiple sclerosis, J.Neurol., 214 (1977),p.153-157.
40. I. Karlsson: Major plasma lipids and their fatty acid composition in multiple sclerosis and other neurological diseases. Acta Neurol. Scand., 47, 1971,p.403-312.
41. J.C. Stoof et al.: Evaluation of the red blood cell cytopherometric test for the diagnosis of M.S. Acta Neurol. Scand., 56 (1977),p.170-176.
42. J. Clausen and J. Møller: Allergic encephalomyelities induced by brain antigen after deficiency in polyunsaturated fatty acids during myelination. Add. ad Int.Arch. Appl. Immunol., 36, 1969,p.224-233.
43. J. Mertin and C J Meade: Relevance of fatty acids in multiple sclerosis. Brit. Med.Bull., 33, 1977,p.67-71.
44. A.N. Davison and M Louise Cuzner: Immunochemistry and biochemistry of myelin. Brit. Med. Bull., 33, 1977,p.60-66.
45. H.M. Wisniewski: Immunopathology of demyelination in autoimmune diseases and virus infections. Brit. Med.Bull., 33, 1972,p.54-59.
46. Libuse Stankova et al.: Leukocyte ascorbate and glutathione: Potential capacity for inactivating oxidants and free radicals. J. reticuloendoth. Soc., 21, 1977, p.97-102.
47. W.M. Tsang et al.: Relationship between plasma and lymphocyte linoleate in multiple sclerosis. J. Neurol. Neurosurg. Psychiat., 39 (1976),p.767-771.
48. R.H. Kimberlin et al.: An experimental examination of the scrapie agent in cell membrane mixtures. J.Comp. Path., 81, 1971,p.383-391.
49. R.H. Kimberlin, ed.: Slow virus at animals and man, 1976. p.209-357.
50. G.D. Hunter: Scrapie. Progr. Med. Virol., 18, 1974,p.289-306.
51. G.D. Hunter et al.: Viral and non-viral properties of the scrapie agent. Ann. clin. res., 5, 1973,p.262-267.
52. D.A. Haig and M.C. Clarke: Multiplication of the scrapie agent. Nature, 234 (Nov. 12, 1971),p.106-107.
53. G.D. Hunter, G.C. Millson: The scrapie agent - the present position about its nature. Recent advances in clinical virology, 1977 (ed. by A.P.Materson),p.61-78.
54. R.E. Kast: Introduction to the scrapie diseases: Self-replicating agents surviving standard autoclaving for an hour and 10% formalin for a year. Materia medica Polona, 8, 1976,p.3-12.
55. A.M. Denman et al.: Virus infections of lymphoreticular cells on auto-immune diseases. Transplant. Rev., 31, 1976, p.79-115.
56. E.J. Field et al.: Measles, multiple sclerosis and encephalitogenic factor. The Lancet, 2, 1972,p.337 (letter to the editor).

57. E.J. Field and J.R. McDermott: Measles and multiple sclerosis. The Lancet, Feb 17, 1973,p.376-377 (letter to the editor).
58. E. Mix et al.: Pathogenesis of multiple sclerosis. The Lancet, June 1975,p.1302-1303.
59. E. Norrby and B. Vandvik: Relationship between measles virus specific antibodies and oligoclonal IgG in the cerebrospinal fluid in patients with multiple sclerosis. Neurology, 25, May 1975,p.493 (abstract).
60. B. Vandvik: Oligoclonal immunoglobulins and virus-specific antibodies in subacute sclerosing panencephalitis and multiple sclerosis. Thesis, Oslo, 1977.
61. H.S. Mickel and J Horbar: The importance of phospholipase A in prostaglandin biosynthesis. Lipids, 9, 1974,p.68-71.
62. R.J. Flower and G.J. Blackwell: The effect of peroxidized arachidonic acid upon human platelets aggregation. Biochim. biophys. Acta. (Amst.) 326 (1973),p.448-461.
63. D.H. Nugteren and E Hazelhof: Isolation and properties of intermediates in prostaglandine biosynthesis. Biochim. biophys. Acta (Amst.) 326 (1973),p.448-461.
64. K.C. Srivastava et al.: The synthesis of prostaglandine in platelets from patients with multiple sclerosis. Acta Neurol. Scand., 51, 1975,p.193-199.

114

Selenium — A Trace Element of Great Significance for the Health of Livestock

Göran Jönson and Bo Pehrson

The interest of veterinary medicine in Se was initially in its toxic effects. Se poisoning (selenosis) has been reported in horse, pig, ruminants and poultry. In cattle selenosis occurs in two forms, one with more acute onset, known in the Anglo-Saxon literature as blind-staggers, the other more chronic, called alkali disease (Rosenberger 1970).

At places with extremely high Se contents in the soil the possibility of keeping livestock at all is reported to be very limited. At such places the Se concentration in the soil may amount to more than 100 ppm, and certain plants may contain 1,000 - 10,000 ppm in the dry matter.

There are plants which absorb Se selectively, so that toxic effects may occur at very much lower levels in the soil than those qouted above. These plants may in such case increase the concentration of Se to levels exceeding 200 ppm of the dry matter, which is undoubtly a toxic content.

If the soil is rich in Se, it will not only be the specifically Se-absorbing plants that constitute a risk. Ordinary fodder-plants as well (grass and cereals) may in such cases contain sufficient Se to cause poisoning. It is calculated that contents exceeding 1 ppm Se of the dry matter of fodder-plants may produce symptoms, but that the risk is pronounced only at more than 5 ppm.

In Sweden there is at present a prohibition against addition of Se to animal fodder. This prohibition derives from the time when the toxic effects of Se were well known, but its significance as an essential trace element practically unknown. A suspected relation between excess of Se and cancer (Nelson et al. 1943) is likely to have greatly influenced the decision to impose the prohibition. Nelson's conclusuions have been seriously questioned (see Frost 1971).

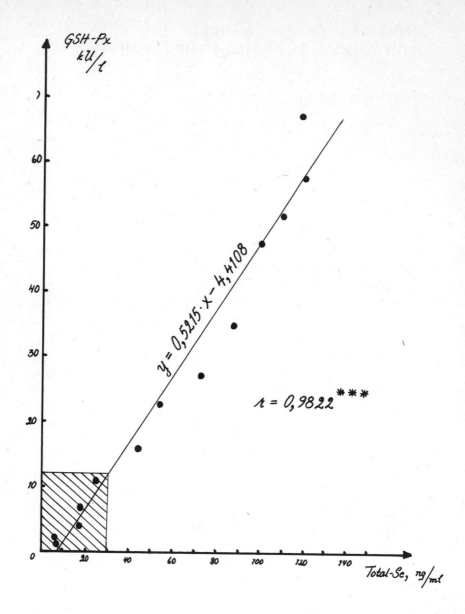

Fig. 1. Correlation between selenium in whole blood and glutathione peroxidase in erythocytes of cattle. Marked area indicates risky zone for muscle degeneration.

Fig. 2. Activity of glutathione peroxidase (GSH-Px) in erythrocytes of young cattle from different parts of Sweden. Solely home-produced fodder had been given for at least 3 months.

117

The first evidence that Se is not only a toxic substance but also an essential trace element was presented in 1957, when Schwarz & Foltz showed Se to be an important constituent in a Factor 3 of earlier unknown composition, which could prevent liver degeneration in rats. In the same year it was shown that Se could prevent a disease in poultry called exudative diathesis (Patterson et al. 1957), and that a relationship existed between Se deficiency and a frequently occurring, acute liver degeneration in pigs, called hepatosis dietetica (Eggert et al. 1957). In the following year came the first report that Se had a prophylactic effect on muscle degeneration in lambs (Muth et al. 1958). Since then numerous papers have confirmed the essential function of Se in the animal body. Vitamin E has also been proved to have a high aetiological and pathogenetic significance in these diseases. An importance is also ascribed to sulphurous amino acids and unsaturated lipids.

The main emphasis in this paper will be on muscle degeneration in cattle. But it should be pointed out that Se-vitamin E deficiency in the form of muscle degeneration is a highly important problem also in foals and lambs in Sweden. On the other hand, in the past 10 years there has hardly been any problem with the Se-vitamin E complex in pigs. The radical structural reorganization of Swedish pig-breeding at the beginning of the 1960s resulted in almost total disappearance of these diseases. Through an almost complete change-over from solely home-produced fodder to factory-produced fodder containing imported elements, the Se contents in diets increased very markedly. This will be seen from Table 1, which also shows that the commercial concentrates marketed in Sweden, containing imported feeds, add at least 10 times as much Se to the animal diet as ordinary Swedish cereal.

In contrast to the situation among pigs, the number of cases of muscle degeneration in cattle has increased in recent years. In certain forms of cattle-breeding there has been a change to a diet based solely on home-produced fodder. The selenium supply may then be so scanty as to involve a considerable risk of muscle degeneration.

Muscle degeneration is well known in many countries. Even if there are no comparable incidence figures it may be stated that the Nordic countries are among the areas where the risk is greatest. There have been very great problems in Finnish Österbotten. The crops in Österbotten are at least as deficient in Se as those in Sweden. An admixture of Se in mineral fodder for cattle has therefore been permitted in Finland and has led to a heavy reduction in the incidence of disease.

Apart from muscle degeneration, cattle may be affected by liver degeneration caused by lack of Se and vitamin E. From the USA it has been reported that so-called saw-dust liver is an expression of this deficiency (Todd & Krook 1966).

In all metabolic processes a number of products are formed which have a potential toxic action on living cells. Among them are several peroxides, among which hydrogen peroxide and lipid peroxides are considered to be most important. If the peroxides are formed on too large a scale and/or if they are not sufficiently effectively decomposed, cell damage arises.

The protective effect of vitamin E and of Se against cell damage is synergistic, but not identical. Whereas vitamin E exercises its protective effect only on the cell membrane, Se protects both cell membrane and cell content. Our present knowledge suggests that vitamin E acts by preventing the formation of peroxides, while Se catalyses the decomposition of peroxides (Hoekstra 1974).

The possibilities of making Se analyses on biological material have for a long time been limited by difficulties of analytical technique. The introduction of new methods of analysis in the form of refined fluorimetry and isotope technique in the last decade have enhanced the technical means for analysis to a great extent, but high costs of analysis have nevertheless placed a limit on the practical possibilities of investigating the Se status of animals. During the 1970s, however, the situation has markedly improved, since it has been found that determination of the enzyme glutathione peroxidase (GSH-Px) reflects the selenium status of the body with a high degree of reliability. In all probability the GSH-Px determination is preferable to the total Se analysis also from other than economic points of view, since the work of Flohe (1971), among others, has shown that Se exercises its probably main biological activity in the form of GSH-Px.

GSH-Px has been found in varying quantities in most of the body organs and tissues and is so abundantly represented in the erythrocytes that ordinary heparin blood is an appropriate test medium. The analyses are inexpensive and technically simple.

Since GSH-Px determinations were introduced in the USA by Rotruck et al. (1973), several studies have been made which reveal a very close correlation of Se in the blood of ruminants (Allen et al. 1975, Anderson & Patterson 1976, Wilson & Judson 1976). The study illustrated in Fig. 1 confirms this correlation still further. If the GSH-Px values in Fig. 1 are related to what, in the available literature (Rosenberger 1970), is indicated as deficiency values for total Se content in the blood of cattle, then GSH-Px values below 12 kU per litre red blood cells should involve a great risk of muscle degeneration. This conforms well with our practical experience, which shows that all examined animals with muscle degeneration had values below 12 kU. In studying Fig. 1 it should be observed that highly elevated total selenium values were not investigated in respect of GSH-Px. If such values had been included in the correlation test, it is possible that the straight-rising correlation line would have been deflected, as the formation of an enzyme would not generally be likely to increase above a given optimal level. In this respect, however, GSH-Px appears to possess a surprising characteristic. For Hafeman et al. (1974) found in experiments with increasing amount of Se in the feed to rats that the GSH-Px values in the blood continued to rise even when the amount of Se in the feed was increased above what is generally considered to be an adequate level.

Earlier studies on cereals have indicated that Sweden is a pronouncedly Se-deficient area (Lindberg 1968). Fig. 2 shows a more extensive survey of Sweden's Se conditions, carried out by means of GSH-Px analyses on young cattle which for at least 3 months before the test had been fed solely on grass. They could thus be presumed to reflect the Se content in the home-produced crop.

Altogether 668 animals from 136 herds in 32 geologically representative areas were examined. The study confirmed that Sweden is predominantly a pronounced deficiency area as

120

regards selenium in crops. Of the herds examined 56 per cent had values below 6 kU and 31 per cent values between 6 and 12 kU, i.e. altogether 87 per cent were classified as belonging to Se-deficiency areas. Normal or relatively high values (12-60 kU) existed in 12 per cent, being strikingly high (>60 kU) in only one of the herds.

The results agreed largely with those expected by geological experts. The areas with consistently low GSH-Px values were thus in regions with a fairly uniform soil species structure for each area, affected by acidic bedrock. In areas with more complicated geological condition, affected especially by schistose rock species, there were comparatively large variations.

As a curiosity it may be mentioned that reindeer on mountain pasture exhibited high values (>60 kU). This indicates that parts of the mountain flora consist of plants with the ability to accumulate Se. This assumption is confirmed by the fact that reindeer in captivity had values barely half as high.

REFERENCES

Allen, W.M., W.H. Parr, P.H. Anderson, S. Berrett, R. Bradley & D.S.P. Patterson: Selenium and the activity of glutathione peroxidase in bovine erythrocytes. Vet. Rec. 1975, 96, 360-361.

Anderson, P.H. & D.S.P. Patterson: Glutathione peroxidase in ruminants and susceptibility to nutritional myopathy. Proc. third international conference on production disease in farm animals, Wageningen Sept. 13-16, 1976, 129-131.

Eggert, R.G., E. Patterson, W.T. Akers & E.L.R. Stokstad: The role of vitamin E and selenium in the nutrition of the pig. J. Anim. Sci., 1957, 16, 1037.

Flohe, L.: Die Glutathionperoxidase: Enzymologie und biologische Aspekte. Klin. Wschr., 1971, 49, 669-683.

Frost, D.V.: The case for selenite as a feed additive. Feedstuffs, 1971, 43, July 31.

Hafeman, D.G., R.A. Sunde & W.G. Hoekstra.: Effect of dietary selenium on erythrocyte and liver glutathione peroxidase in the rat. J. Nutr., 1974, 104, 580-587.

Hoekstra, W.G.: Biochemical role of selenium. In: Trace element metabolism in animals - 2. University Park Press. Baltimore 1974, 61—77.

Lindberg, P.: Selenium determination in plant and animal material, and in water. Acta vet. scand. 1968. Suppl. 23.

Mikkelsen, T. & M.A. Hansen: Ernæringsbetinget muskeldegenerasjon hos lam. Nord. Vet.-Med. 1968, 20, 402—419.

Muth, O.H., J.E. Oldfield, L.F. Remmert & J.R. Schubert: Effects of selenium and vitamin E on white muscle disease. Science, 1958, 128, 1090.

Nelson, A.A., O.G. Fitzhugh & H.O. Calvery: Liver tumors following cirrhosis caused by selenium in rats. Cancer Res., 1943, 3, 230-236.

Oksanen, H.E. & M. Sandholm: The selenium content of Finnish forage crops. J. Sci. Agr. Soc. Finl., 1970, 42, 250-253.

Patterson, E.L., R. Milstrey & E.L.R. Stokstad: Effect of selenium in preventing exudative diathesis in chicks. Proc. Soc. exp. Biol. Med. 1957, 95, 617-620.

Rosenberger, G. In: Krankheiten des Rindes, Paul Parey, Berlin & Hamburg 1970.

Rotruck, J.T., A.L. Pope, H.E. Ganther, A.B. Swanson, D.G. Hafeman & W.G. Hoekstra: Selenium: Biochemical role as a component of glutathione peroxidase. Science, 1973, 179, 588-590.

Schwarz, K. & C.M. Foltz: Selenium as an integral part of factor 3 against dietary necrotic liver degeneration. J. Amer. Chem. Soc., 1957, 79, 3292-3293.

Tood, G.C. & L. Krook: Nutritional hepatic necrosis in beef cattle. Path. vet., 1966, 3, 379-400.

Ullrey, D.E.: The selenium-deficiency problem in animal agriculture. In: Trace element metabolism in animals. - 2. University Park Press. Baltimore 1974, 275—293.

Wilson, P.S. & G.J. Judson: Glutathione peroxidase activity in bovine and ovine erythrocytes in relation to blood selenium concentration. Brit. vet. J., 1976, 132, 428-434.

Table 1. Selenium content in animal fodder (ppm of dry matter). To avoid symptoms of SE-deficiency 0,1 ppm in the dry matter is necessary.

Fodder	Number of samples	Mean value	Range	Reference
Cereals, Sweden	56	0.013	0.004—0.046	Lindberg 1968
Cereals, Finland	52	0.007	0.002—0.085	Oksanen & Sandholm 1970
Cereals, Imported to Sweden*	7	0.376	0.052—1.300	Lindberg 1968
Corn, USA	176	0.087	0.010—2.030	Ullrey 1974
Hay. Sweden	12	0.023	0.011—0.034	Lindberg 1968
Hay, Finland	61	0.014	0.002—0.048	Oksanen & Sandholm 1970
Hay, Norway	15	0.013	0.004—0.028	Mikkelsen & Aas Hansen 1968
Proteinrich concentrates imported to Sweden**	7	0.548	0.046—1.520	Lindberg 1968
Commercial concentrates, Sweden	13	0.164	0.102—0.220	Lindberg 1968
Commercial concentrates, Norway	4	0.220	0.120—0.310	Mikkelsen & Aas Hansen 1968
Commercial concentrates, USA	23	0.172	0.030—0.490	Ullrey 1974
Fishmeal	6	1.943	1.470—2.450	Lindberg 1968
Drinking-water µg/lit.	8	0.12	0.06 —0.15	Lindberg 1968

* Argentina n = 1, Canada n = 1, Turkey n = 1, USA n = 3
** Africa n = 2, Cyprus n = 1, Russia n = 1, Germany n = 1

Flurosis in Farm Animals in Iceland Related to Volcanic Eruptions

P. A. Palsson, G. Georgsson, G. Petursson

I

In Iceland very active volcanic areas are found. More than 30 different volcanoes are known to have been active in historical times. A number of other volcanoes are known that have been inactive for more than one thousand years but could possibly become active again.

It therefore seems realistic to anticipate volcanic activity in Iceland at certain intervals in the future.

During the twentieth century there have been some 13 volcanic eruptions, four of which can be characterized as major ones.

For centuries farmers in Iceland have been familiar with diseases of animals occurring in relation to volcanic eruptions. These diseases mainly affected the bones and teeth of the animals, and their various manifestations all had different names in the Icelandic language (öskueitrun, öskutönn, gostönn, gaddur, standgaddur, snidgaddur, tvöfaldur gaddur, skert, beinskert, fætlur).

In historical times there have been 16 different eruptions of the notorious volcano Hekla. I will confine this report to the last five and the harmful effect they have had on farm animals.

The eruptions of Hekla usually seem to follow a rather similar pattern according to S. Thorarinsson (13). Starting with a violent Plinian explosive phase, the eruption column then sometimes reaches the stratosphere, but lasts only from one to several hours, during which a high proportion of the tephra (ash) is produced.

Depending on the prevailing wind during this first phase of the eruption, the spread of the volcanic ash can be very great, covering hundreds of square kilometers within a few hours.

The ash layer is of variable thickness and coarseness. Sometimes the ash covers the vegetation entirely; however, at greater distances from the volcano the ash layer is usually much thinner, but at the same time more fine-grained and therefore even more dangerous for the animals (14).

Because the volcanic ash often has a high content of fluorine, the pastures, especially at the beginning, are dangerous for grazing animals.

After the violent initial phase of the eruption, the activity decreases rapidly, and the flow of lava starts and often continues for months with varying intensity. During this period minor ash eruptions sometime occur.

II

The first eruption of Hekla to be described here started on 13 February 1693 and lasted for 7 months. Within a few hours the tephra had been carried towards the north-west part of Iceland, destroying or damaging more than 50 farms. Two reports, one by the farmer Oddur Eiriksson (1640-1719) (2), the other by the Rev. Benedikt Pjetursson (1640-1727) (9) describe the effects of the volcanic ash on the teeth of farm animals. The following account is written by Oddur Eiriksson in 1695: "The following autumn and winter (1694) people noticed that the teeth of young sheep had yellow spots and some dark ones; in some animals the teeth were all black. The teeth fell out in some cases but little round pointed teeth came up afresh, like the teeth of a dog; teeth affected with the spots turned soft so they could be cut with a knife like wood.

In some animals the gingiva peeled away from around the incisors and molars. Those which had the yellow spots recovered and their teeth turned white. People thought that this was due to the sand-fall from Hekla. Both young cattle and young ponies got yellow patches on their teeth. But ponies and sheep which shed teeth that year, got a blue-black streak over any new teeth that developed, and because of this their age could be told as long as they lived. Many called them "ash-teeth".

Dental lesions similar to those described here have repeatedly been observed in connection with volcanic eruptions in Iceland and are considered to be caused by the high fluorine content of the volcanic ash.

III

On 5. April 1766 the next eruption of Hekla started and lasted for two years.

During the first few hours the tephra fall was very heavy, covering an area of approx. 34,000 km², about one third of the country. Heavy damage was sustained on farm land both in the northern part and in the southern part of the country, resulting in the death of farm animals by the thousands.

A description of the toxic effect of volcanic ash on farm animals is given by Hannes Finnsson (1739-1796) in his report on this and other volcanic eruptions (4, 5). In particular he describes the conspicuous changes of the molars in young animals called "gaddur", which is an irregular growth of the molars, some of which grow into sharp points or edges that fit roughly into corresponding defects in the opposite row of molars.

The affected animals were very sensitive to cold water. Finnsson also observed that the offspring from affected sheep remained healthy and the disease was never transmitted to healthy sheep. A description is also given of the cure used by farmers: cutting or sawing the spikes off the molars in affected sheep in order to restore normal mastication.

IV

The next eruption of Hekla began in September 1845 and lasted for almost 7 months. The main tephra fall lasted for about 4 hours covering vast areas southeast of the volcano, and the fine-grained ash was carried as far as the Faroe Islands, the Shetlands, and the Orkneys. Later during this eruption serious damage was caused by the fall of black fine-grained ash in districts west and northwest of the volcano.

There are several detailed reports describing diseases of farm animals caused by the ash from this eruption (1, 7, 10, 11).

The Danish botanist J.C. Schythe (1814-1877) (11) and Rev.

125

Johann Björnsson (1810-1847) (1) and several others have described acute fluorosis found in cattle on the first days after the eruption started. They have also given detailed descriptions of various dental lesions which attacked only the permanent teeth of young animals that had not shed their deciduous teeth prior to the eruption. The incisors were studded with dark spots and decayed quickly. The molars became deformed, which hurt the opposite jaw, making normal chewing difficult. In many animals both young and old, marked lesions of the bones were found, which caused stiffness and lameness. The hoofs of animals in districts where the coarse volcanic ash was abundant soon became so worn and damaged that they could hardly walk, and ponies had to be shod to protect their hoofs.

At the Royal Veterinary College in Copenhagen there is a collection of bones of adult sheep which grazed in the vicinity of Hekla during the eruption of 1845. K. Roholm (1902-1948) (10) in his classic monograph, Fluorine Intoxication, was the first one to describe these bones and determine their content of fluorine. On the surface of all the bones characteristic periosteal exostosis of porous and brittle osteous tissue had been formed, in some instances covering most of the normal bone. The fluorine content of these bones was high, 4400-20,600 p.p.m.F, confirming that these bone lesions were caused by fluorine. Roholm could produce similar lesions in animals experimentally by feeding them hay mixed with NaF.

V

On 29 March 1947 the next eruption of Hekla started. In the violent initial phase the eruption column reached a height of 30,000 meters and during the first hours the districts southeast of the volcano were covered with coarse ash. The most fine-grained ash was carried as far away as Finland. This eruption lasted for 13 months, and during the summer of 1947 minor amounts of new black fine-grained ash were repeatedly noticed in the vicinity of the volcano (13).

Now for the first time it was possible to determine the fluoride content of the volcanic ash. It was found to vary within comparatively narrow limits, i.e. 70 to 110 p.p.m. F, the finest fraction (<0.062 mm) containing six times more fluoride than the coarsest one (>0.25 mm) (14).

During the first weeks of the eruption some sheep succumbed to a disease which might well have been acute fluorosis. Three to four months after the beginning of the eruption signs of chronic fluorosis were found in a high percentage of sheep belonging to farms in the vicinity of Hekla. Stiffness and intermittent lameness was common in nursing ewes, and irregular small nodules on the lower jaw and the legs were often found. These nodules, which were firm but tender, regressed, however, and often disappeared the following winter. Later it was found that many sheep from these flocks born one year prior to the eruption or just after the eruption developed lesions of their permanent teeth, which showed irregular wear resulting in the formation of sharp edges or spikes, which interfered with normal chewing. Many of these sheep were therefore destroyed. The fluoride content of bones from these sheep was found to be approx. 7000 p.p.m.

Only a few grass samples were collected from affected areas. The content of fluorine was lower than expected or 25 p.p.m. on the average.

By mixing volcanic ash collected from this eruption with water and hay and feeding this to sheep for six months, mild fluorosis could be produced experimentally.

The studies and experience from this eruption indicated that even by consuming only 1.5 to 2.0 mg fluorides per kg. body weight per day Icelandic sheep are likely to develop mild chronic fluorosis. (12).

VI

The last eruption of Hekla began on 5 May 1970. During the first hours volcanic ash fell over a wide area northwest of the volcano, as shown in Fig. 1.

Diseases of farm animals related to this eruption have been studied by Georgsson, G. & Petursson, G. (3). Analysis of ash samples taken on the first days after the eruption showed a high content of water soluble fluorides, 1400-2000 p.p.m. Owing to heavy rain, the fluoride content in the ash decreased rapidly,

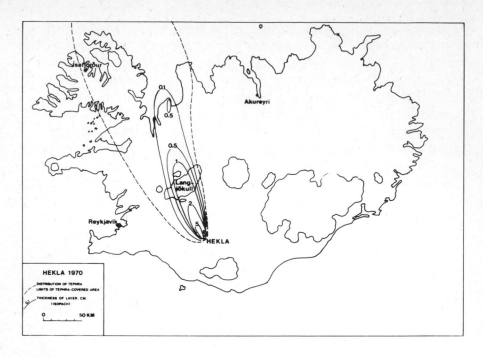

Fig. 1. Distribution of ash. (By Sig. Thorarinsson.)

so that three weeks later only 1-2% remained in the ash.

Surface water showed a marked increase of fluorine values; 4 to 70 p.p.m. were found in stagnant water and in running surface water values of 10 p.p.m. were found. Within a few days the fluorine content declined, however, to almost normal values.

The vegetation became heavily polluted. Samples collected immediately after the beginning of the eruption showed a fluorine content of 4300 p.p.m.

Analyses of grass carried out at regular intervals showed that the content fell rapidly, so that in 35 to 40 days the fluorine content in grass was less than 30 p.p.m. The drop could be attributed to the heavy rainfall and the rapid growth of the grass at this time of the year. (Fig. 2).

Animals that were not housed were therefore only exposed to grass containing excessive fluorine for 5 to 6 weeks.

Animals grazing in the fields as the volcanic ash was falling

128

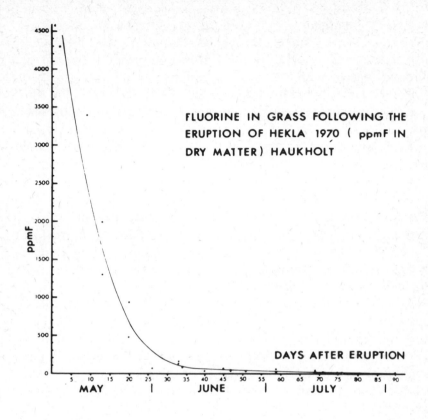

FLUORINE IN GRASS FOLLOWING THE
ERUPTION OF HEKLA 1970 (ppmF IN
DRY MATTER) HAUKHOLT

were frightened and restless, perhaps because the ash caused marked irritation both of the eyes and the nostrils.

Already one or two days after the beginning of the eruption sheep on many farms fell ill. The signs were rather indefinite - loss of appetite, drowsiness, general prostration, intermittent lameness, and occasionally inability to stand or walk. Blood samples showed low serum calcium levels in many cases, with the lowest one recorded being 5.30 mg%. The fluoride content of the urine was increased, with values from 30 to 60 p.p.m. In some instances gastrointestinal symptoms were the predominating ones. After 2 to 3 weeks sheep started to shed wool.

Ewes in their late pregnancy and poorly fed sheep seemed to be most susceptible. If these animals were taken off the polluted grassfields and housed, given calcium injections, mineral mixtures, concentrates and hay of good quality they often recovered after a few days. However, affected ewes often aborted or gave birth to dead or weak lambs at normal term.

Ponies left on the polluted pastures lost their appetite and became dull. Foal and pregnant mares seemed to be most susceptible, with death sometimes occurring.

In a few instances acute fluorosis in cattle could be traced back to the use of contaminated drinking water just after the ashfall.

Autopsy findings of sheep that had succumbed during the first days are consistent with those of acute fluorine intoxication. Considering the high content of fluoride in surface water, it is thought that some sheep might have ingested as much as 100 mg fluoride pr.kg.pr. day. This is considered to be in the range of an acute lethal dose.

Since the sheep had not been exposed to a high intake of fluorine for more than 5 to 6 weeks at most, it was unlikely that fluorotic bone lesions would be found. Clinical examination of approx. 700 sheep on different farms revealed only slight periostal lesions in less than 10 of these sheep.

Analyses of bones from five-month-old lambs, yearlings and adults showed a marked increase in the fluoride content, especially in the young sheep (Table 1).

Regular examination of the teeth of young sheep carried out in the year following the eruption revealed lesions of the incisors in some of them.

Table 1. Results of fluorine analysis of bones (ppm fluorine in ash).

	Number	Mean	S.D.	Lowest Value	Highest Value	Normal Mean	S.D.
Lambs	47	698	348	165	1570	116	60
Yearlings	26	1683	907	710	3900	560	
Adult Sheep	13	1329	401	850	2000	830	

130

These lesions were most often found in incisors that erupted 1/2 to 1 year after the sheep had been exposed to heavy ash contamination on the pastures. These lesions were most frequently found in sheep which were two years of age when exposed to the ash (Table 2). Dental lisions found on the molars were minor ones only.

Table 2. Dental fluorosis of sheep following the eruption of Hekla in 1970.

Incisors	Eruption of teeth in months after exposure to high fluorine	Total number of teeth observed	Normal	Questionable effect	Fluorotic lesions
I_1	1–5	291	287	4	0
I_3	4–9	154	109	6	39(25,3%)
I_2	9–13	186	165	5	16(8,6%)
I_1	13–17	104	99	5	0

Incisors of ponies that had been exposed to the ash on their pastures were often severely affected. Usually only one pair of incisors was affected, those erupting one year after the exposure.

The bone and dental lesions found in farm animals in Iceland exposed to volcanic ash are apparently similar to lesions described in many other countries as industrial fluorosis in animals occurring in restricted areas adjacent to certain industrial plants. (6, 8).

REFERENCES

1. Björnsson, J.: Ny Felagsrit, VI: 183-202, VII: 234-241, VII: 185-186, 1846-1847.
2. Eiriksson, O.: Annales Islandici II (1400-1800): 299-300. Reykjavik 1927-1932.
3. Georgsson, G. and G. Petursson: Fluorosis of sheep caused by the Hekla eruption in 1970. Fluoride, 2: 58-66, 1972.
4. Finnsson, H.: Efterretning om Tildragelserne ved Bjerget Hekla ud i Island i April og følgende Måneder 1766. Copenhagen 1767.
5. Finnsson, H.: Um mannfækkun af hallærum a Islandi: 120-122, Reykjavik 1970.

6. Flatla, J.L.: Atmosfæriske forurensninger fra industrier som årsak til sygdom hos husdyr. Finsk veterinärskrift, 12: 61-72, 1967.
7. Melsted, P.: Ny Felagsrit, VI: 202-210, 1846.
8. Obel, Anna-Lisa: A literary review on bovine fluorosis. Acta vet. Scand., 12, 151-163, 1971.
9. Petursson, B.: Annales Islandici II (1400-1800), 535-536. Reykjavik 1927-1932.
10. Roholm, K.: Fluorine intoxication, A clinical hygienic study. Copenhagen and London 1937.
11. Schythe, J.C.: Hekla og dens sidste Udbrud den 2den September 1845, En Monographi. Copenhagen 1847.
12. Sigurdsson, B. & P.A. Palsson: Fluorosis of farm animals during the Hekla eruption of 1947-1948. The eruption of Hekla 1947-48, Part III, 3, 1-12, Reykjavik 1957.
13. Thorarinsson, S.: The eruption of Hekla 1947-1948, I. The eruptions of Hekla in historical times, Reykjavik 1967.
14. Thorkelsson, G.: Some reflections on fluorides of the ash and water during the eruption. The eruption of Hekla 1947-1948, Part III, 2, 11-13, Reykjavik 1957.

Possible Environmental Risk Factors in the Causation of Thyroid Cancer in Iceland

Ólafur Bjarnason

I. ICELAND AND ICELANDERS

Iceland is an island located in the northern Atlantic with a total area of 103,000 km² (40,000 square miles). The island reaches up to the Arctic circle and the eastermost point is long. 13° 29'W; the shortest distance to Norway is 970 km.

The ground is volcanic, with huge lava fields, and the country is very mountainous with mountain peaks up to a height of 21000 m. There has been great volcanic activity in the past and up to the present time.

The original settlement of Iceland in the latter part of the 9th and the beginning of the 10th century was mainly made from Norway, with some minor admixture from southern Sweden and Denmark. To the main Scandinavian stock there has also been some admixture of celtic blood (2). After Iceland was fully settled, very little immigration occured from outside.

At the present time the country is very sparsely populated. According to the National Registry, the whole population, as of 1 December 1977, was 222,055. This gives an average density of 2.2 innhabitants per square kilometer, which is the lowest in Europe. Today most of the people live on the shores of the island close to the sea, with a much smaller proportion in the inland valleys. Fish forms a considerable part of diet of the population, and the iodide content of the Icelandic milk is unusually high (1).

II. THE THYROID GLAND OF THE ICELANDERS

In 1940 Julius Sigurjonsson published his thesis: Studies on the Human Thyroid in Iceland (10).

The main findings of Sigurjonson's studies are drawn up in Table 1 and Table 2, which show, on the one hand, the unusual smallness of the gland and, on the other hand, the high iodine concentration in the fresh gland tissue.

Table 1. Weight of the adult thyroid in Iceland (from J. Sigurjonsson).

Locality	M. 20–79 years		F. 20–81 years	
	No.	Av. Weight of thyroid	No.	Av. Weight of thyroid
Reykjavik	64	13.85 g	46	11.32 g
Iceland (outside Reykjavik)	80	13.90 g	72	11.54 g

Table 2. Iodine content of the human thyroid in Iceland (from J. Sigurjonsson).

No. of cases	Age in years	Mg. Iodine pr. 1 g fresh weight	Total Iodine Mg.
M.73	20–79	0.962	12.747
F. 55	20–81	0.861	9.838

More recent studies on thyroid biochemistry and physiology of the Icelanders have shown that the level of plasma inorganic iodide is high (6) and serum TSH levels low (8).

III. THYROID CARCINOMA IN ICELAND

According to statements in the older literature (see, e.g. 7), one would have expected the incidence of thyroid carcinoma to be very low in Iceland with the high iodine content of the food. It was therefore a surprise to the present author to find that the incidence of thyroid carcinoma was unusually high. This finding was first presented at the XIV Scandinavian Congress of Pathology and Microbiology held in Oslo in 1964 (3)

134

and later presented in Edinburgh in 1966 (4). This finding was verified by a joint study undertaken by the Cancer Registries of four Nordic Countries (9). Table 3, quoted from this study, shows a comparison of the incidence rates.

Table 3. Carcinoma of thyroid. Age adjusted incidence rates per 100,000.

Sex	Country	All ages
M.	Finland	1.0
	Iceland	2.6
	Norway	1.1
	Sweden	1.3
F.	Finland	2.4
	Iceland	7.7
	Norway	2.4
	Sweden	3.1

A further collaborative study was undertaken by pathologists from the same Nordic Countries. They reviewed 696 cases of thyroid cancer reported to the national cancer registries and classified them according to the WHO histologic classification of thyroid tumours (5). One of the findings of this study is that the bulk of the Icelandic cases is of the papillary type or 62.6%.

A further collaborative study, using thyroid cancer material from the iodiderich area of Iceland for comparison with a relatively iodide-low area in North-East Scotland, has shown that the papillary type is much higher in the Icelandic than the Scottish material, whereas the reverse is true for the follicular type. The main conclusion to be drawn from this study seems to be that a high dietary intake of iodide is associated with a high incidence of papillary carcinoma, and a low dietary iodide intake is associated with a relatively high incidence of follicular carcinoma (11).

Finally, a comparison has been made between the incidence of thyroid cancer in different areas of Iceland, showing an incidence of 9.2 pr 100,000 pr year in the western part of the

Table 4. Incidence of thyroid cancer in Iceland in different areas.

Area	No. of cases			Population 1. Dec. 1974			Incidence 100,000/year		
	F.	M.	Total	F.	M.	Total	F.	M.	Total
Reykjavik	117	27	144	43 471	41 301	84 772	13.5	3.3	8.5
Reykjanes	26	9	35	21 602	22 342	43 944	6.0	2.0	4.0
Western District	35	9	44	11 293	12 509	23 802	15.5	3.6	9.2
Northern District	33	13	46	16 439	17 223	33 662	10.0	3.8	6.8
Eastern District	5	1	6	5 586	6 333	11 919	4.5	0.8	2.5
Southern District	21	5	26	8 731	9 798	18 529	12.0	2.6	7.0
Total	237	64	301	107 122	109 506	216 628	11.1	2.9	6.9

country, where the incidence is highest, and an incidence of 2.5 pr 100,000 pr year in the eastern part of the country, where the incidence is lowest (see Table 4).

An explanation of this significant difference in incidence between different districts in Iceland is hard to find at the present time.

REFERENCES

1. Alexander, W.D., Th.V. Gudmundsson, M.M. Bluhm & R.McG. Harden: Studies of iodine metabolism in Iceland. Acta endocr. Kbh., 46 (1964), 679-683.
2. Bjarnason, Ó., V. Bjarnason, J.H. Edwards, S. Fridriksson, M. Magnusson, A.E. Mourant & D. Tills: The blood groups of Icelanders. Ann. hum. Genet. 36 (1973), 425-458.
3. Bjarnason, Ó.: Carcinoma of the thyroid in Iceland. Proceedings of the XIV Scandinavian Congress of Pathology and Microbiology, 123-124, Oslo 1964.
4. Bjarnason, Ó.: Cancer incidence in Iceland. In: Shivas, A.A. (Ed.). Racial and geographical factors in tumour incidence, 118-131. Edinburgh 1967.
5. Bjarnason, Ó., K. Franssila, T. Normann, N. Ringertz & E. Sexen: Observer variation in histologic classification of thyroid cancer. Acta path. microbiol. scand. (In press).
6. Crooks, J., M.J. Tulloch, A.C. Turnbull: Comparative incidence of goitre in pregnancy in Iceland and Scotland. Lancet 2 (1967), 625-627.

7. Egloff, B.: Bösartige Schilddrusen Geschwulste mit besonderer Berucksichtigung maligner Rezidive primär gutartigen Kröpfe. Schweiz med. Wschr. 91 (1961), 424-430.
8. Hedley, A.j., B. Thjodleifsson, D. Donald, J. Beck Swanson, J. Crooks, M.J. Chesters & R. Hall: Thyroid function in normal subjects in Iceland and Northeast Scotland. Clinic. Endocri., 7 (1977), 377-382.
9. Ringertz, N. (Ed.): Cancer incidence in Finland, Iceland, Norway and Sweden. Acta path. microbiol. scand. Sect. A. Suppl. 224, 1971.
10. Sigurjonsson, J.: Studies on the human thyroid in Iceland. Thesis. Reykjavik 1940.
11. Williams, E.D., J. Doniach, O. Bjarnason & W. Michie: Cancer, 39 (1977), 215-222.

Some Speculations on Geomedical Problems in Iceland

Sturla Fredriksson

Human beings, like all living things, are greatly influenced by many factors in the environment. One of the most important is diet, a large part of which is ultimately determined by the soil. The soil contains minerals, which are supplied to plants and, in turn, to the animals higher up on the food chain. Any imbalance of minerals or any toxic substances in the soil can thus have a serious effect on the entire ecosystem, including the health of human beings.

The relationship between soil and plants is rather direct; man's position in this system however, is more complicated. It is especially difficult in modern society to isolate for study the numerous elements which, along with diet, affect man. Isolated communities, confined to a region with a set of unique environmental conditions, are therefore ideal subjects for studying the possible association between disease and environmental factors, such as soil composition.

Such a setting is to be found in Iceland. Along with its geographical isolation, it has specific geological characteristics that distinguish it from the other Nordic countries.

Geologically speaking, Iceland is a relatively young country, its plateaus having been built up only in the last 20 million years.

The basic rock type in Iceland is basaltic, in contrast to the granite and gneiss bedrock of Scandinavia and the sedimentary rock formations in Finland, Denmark, and southern Sweden. Basalt has a higher iron and calcium content than granite does (Table 1). Icelandic bogs are often so rich in iron that the water and vegetation in these areas is unpalatable. The effect of this high iron content on human beings is not known. In the long run it might affect blood status or possibly even blood groups.

Table 1. The chemical composition of igneous rocks.

	Effusive Tholeiite Basalt	Plutonic Alkali Granite
SiO_2	50.83	73.86
TiO_2	2.03	0.20
Al_2O_2	14.07	13.75
Fe_2O_3	2.88	0.78
Feo	9.06	1.13
MnO	0.18	0.05
MgO	6.34	0.26
CaO	10.42	0.72
Na_2O	2.23	3.51
K_2O	0.82	5.13
H_2O	0.91	0.47
P_2O_5	0.23	0.14

(Barth, T.F., 1962 Theoretical Petrology, John Wiley, London.)

Comparative studies of the medical statistics of the Nordic countries have revealed significant variations in the health of these populations. The distribution of certain diseases in Iceland, for example, has a pattern somewhat different from that of other Scandinavian countries (see Table 2).

Table 2. Death rates per 100,000 population average 1970–1975.

	Iceland	Denmark	Finland	Norway	Sweden
Multiple sclerosis	0.1	1.5	0.7	1.2	1.2
Bronchitis emphysema and asthma	9.9	26.8	22.1	14.1	16.2
Congenital All anomalies Spina	8.1	7.9	6.8	7.0	7.2
bifida	0.5	0.2	0.2	0.4	0.3
Diabetes	2.2	13.7	14.5	7.4	18.0

Certain diseases appear to be rarer in Iceland than elsewhere. *Multiple sclerosis*, for instance, seems to have a lower incidence in Iceland than in Scandinavia and Scotland. It has been associated with soils of glacial origin (Warren, 1959) or with low selenium content. *Bronchitis* and *asthma* occur less frequently in Iceland, partly due to the small amount of pollen in the air. The low incidence of *diabetes* may be to some degree genetic, but dietary differences must surely be an important factor. The thyroid gland is relatively smaller in Icelanders. This is no doubt due to the important role of fish in the diet, which is rich in iodine (Sigurjonsson, 1938, 1940). Rheumatic fever is also considered rare (Sigurjonsson, 1943).

On the other hand, the occurrence of stomach cancer has been found to be quite high in Iceland (Dungal, 1961; Bjarnason, 1967). Certain congenital disorders, such as *spina bifida*, seem to be slightly more common. The high occurrence of this deformity could be due to the greater degree of inbreeding in Iceland, but a diet of spoiled potatoes has also been suggested as a possible cause. The incidence of cleft lip and cleft palate in Iceland has been found to be the highest yet observed in any Caucasian population: 2.51 per every 1000 births (Möller, 1964).

Comparative studies of this kind, however, are problematic, because it is difficult to distinguish environmental influence from genetic influences. It is perhaps a more fruitful approach to study variations within a genetically homogenous population like that of Iceland.

Studying the relationship between disease and the environment in Iceland is facilitated by the geological differences between districts. Tertiary basalt layers form the bedrock of the country's east and west sides, but a much younger median zone, formed mainly during the Pleistocene epoch and modified by subsequent volcanic activity, lies like a belt across the island on a northeast to southwest axis. This is a volcanic zone with frequent eruptions. In this medial zone there are also high temperature areas ejecting steam, dissolving rock, and emitting sulphurous fumes. Hot water springs are widespread, and water from these springs is commonly used for consumption. Volcanic activity has, throughout the centuries, affected the health of the population, particularly in the medial zone, which covers about

40% of the total area of Iceland.

The initial catastrophic effects of volcanic eruptions are followed by slower, more gradual reactions in the ecosystem, largely chemical in nature. The various gases like fluoride and sulphur are released into the atmosphere and then dissolved in the water, eventually affecting plants and animals.

Some of these more subtle aspects of the environment deserve investigation, particularly the chemical composition of the soil and water, as well as the vegetation. Analysis of their chemical content reveals the substances that may be transmitted to the human diet and thus affect health.

CHEMICAL ELEMENTS IN THE ECOSYSTEM

Table 3 shows the content of different types of river water in Iceland on the basis of origin. A few more analyses of elements in water, soil and grasses in Iceland may be mentioned.

Fluoride content in grass may be 250 ppm by dry weight shortly following volcanic ash fall (Fridriksson, 1973 and 1975), but in cold tap water it is close to 0.5 ppm F. Air and water are rich in *sulphur* in the volcanic area and soils do not show sulphur deficiency, except in the northern part of Iceland (Sigvaldason, 1967; Helgadottir et al. 1977). Phosphate is generally low in Icelandic soils except in the western peninsula (Palmason, 1978). Grass may contain 0.23 to 0.51 % P (Johannesson, 1961). *Potassium* is sometimes deficient in sandy soil and some peat soils, and grass may contain 0.50 to 3.55 % K in D.M. (Armstrong, 1964 a, b: Olafsson and Eirikson, 1976; Larusson, 1977). *Calcium* content of hay is 0.30 to 0.38 % byt may be 0.41 % Ca in D.M. of hay on soils rich in lime, as on a few farms in the western part of the country (Björnsson, et at. 1975; Annual Report 1976). *Magnesium* seems adequate in the fodder of lambs (Gudmundsson et al., 1976) but may be deficient in dairy cows after calving (Sigurdsson and Thorsteinsson, 1978). *Manganese* content in grass is, on the average, lowest in the southern districts (84 ppm). *Zinc* content in grass ranges from 23 to 35 ppm (Palmason, 1972, Helgadottir and Palmason, 1976). *Copper* deficiency may show up in lambs from ewes feeding on seaweed (Palsson and Grimsson, 1953 and 1954). *Cobalt* values

142

Table 3. Chemical analysis of river water in southern central part of Iceland.

Rivers		pH	mg/l									µg/l				
			HCO_3^-	CO_3^{--}	Na^+	Mg^{2+}	Ca^{2+}	K^+	SO_4^{--}	$Cl-$	SiO_2	NO_3^-	NO_2^-	NH_3	PO_4^{3-}	$F-$
With geothermal water	Varma	7,95	82,8		23,7	4,23	14,8	1,64	15,5	17,4	35,2	133	4,81	58,3	29,0	173
With glacial water	Hvita	7,46	32,5		8,12	1,31	3,66	0,58	5,04	3,86	10,2	93	3,01	32,9	34,2	99
	Thjorsa	7,59	41,8		10,6	1,80	4,67	0,60	6,78	4,68	10,0	139	3,68	39,2	65,2	160
With spring water	Bruara	8,84	17,6	3,92	7,50	0,47	2,64	0,37	4,09	3,97	10,3	175	2.97	30,0	36,2	45

(Rist, S editor 1974 – Efnarannsokn vatns 1973. Orkustofnun Reykjavik.)

may be lower than 0.1 ppm in D.M. of grass on soils rich in lime in the western part of Iceland (Gudmundsson and Thorsteinsson, 1976). *Mercury* may be high (1,000 ppb) in geothermal areas, such as near Geysir in Southern Iceland (Coderre and Steinthorsson, 1977). *Lead* in grass averages 0.8 ppm, but values as high as 19.8 ppm have been obtained in grass growing beside highways (Palmason, 1973). *Boron* and *Molybden* deficiency may be observed on kales and turnips from peat soils (Gudleifsson and Gunnarsson, 1978). *Nitrate* in drinking water from wells in one district on the south central lowland may be as high as 164 ppm, which is 100 times greater than a low average value.

DISTRIBUTION OF DISEASE

A few attempts have been made to show the relationship between the environment and human disease in Iceland. The incidence of stomach cancer, for example, is not evenly distributed throughout Iceland. It is heavily concentrated in the northwestern districts. This has been linked with the heavy consumption of smoked foods in these areas (Dungal, 1961), but certain geomedical considerations should not be ignored. This area is outside the volcanic zone, and its soil is rather low in sulphur. In contrast, the district with the lowest incidence of stomach cancer is situated in a geothermal zone.

The volcanic area of Rangarvallacountry in the south had the lowest cancer incidence. Armstrong (1964, a, b), who compared the environment, soil, water, and diet on farms with cancer and no cancer cases in the northern districts and southern part of the country, did not find any major differences in the element content of water and plants at the farms. He concluded that the validity of testing soil-cancer relationship in this way was questionable, as "the chemical composition of the foodstuffs is subject to a wide range of influencing factors in animal metabolism and lactation, food processing, metal contacts, amounts eaten and personal food preference."

Gudmundsson (1971) found multiple sclerosis accumulated in 3 to 4 zones. He described the environmental characteristics of the different zones and the possible influences.

144

The geographical distribution of the incidence of cleft lip and cleft palate in Iceland was studied by Möller (1969). He accepts the importance of heredity in the occurrence of the malformation, but feels that environmental agents may also play a part. However, he did not find significant differences between areas, although there did appear to be a relatively high incidence in the central-western part of the country as well as in the north-eastern part. It is not obvious what these areas may have in common, except possibly consumption of some local food products.

CONCLUSION

Relationships between soil-plants and man are not necessarily direct, but may be of a high complex nature and dependent upon a proper balance of many elements rather than a single one.

Various organic compounds may have closer connection to disease than simple chemical elements.

In modern society a person's diet consists of a wide variety of food-stuffs with only a fraction deriving from the home soil. The grouping of the incidence of disease is often arbitrary, depending on location of hospitals or municipal divisions which do not necessarily coincide with zones of special environmental conditions.

Finally, man himself is so variable, with his diverse genetic constitution, that he reacts differently to the elements, which further complicates the evaluation of associating environment to disease.

REFERENCES

Annual Reports of the Agricultural Research Institute 10, 1976 pp.93.

Armstrong, R.W. (1964a) Environmental factors involved in studying the relationship between soil elements and disease. Amer. publ. Hlth 54:9 pp. 1536-1544.

. . . . . . (1964b) Spectrographic analyses of pasture grass and drinking water in relation to stomach cancer mortality in Iceland. Acta Agriculturae Acand. 14:1 pp. 65-76.

Barth, T.F. (1962) Theoretical Petrology, John Wiley, London.

Bjarnason, Ó. (1967) Cancer incidence in Iceland. In Racial and geographical factors in tumor incidence. (ed. A.A. Shivas) Edinburgh University Press.

Björnsson, H., Palmason, F., Sigvaldson, J. (1975) Jord, gödsling och gräsproduktion. NJF 57 pp. 169-174.

Coderre, J.A. and Steinthorsson, S. (1977) Natural concentrations of mercury in Iceland. Geochimica et Cosmochimica Acta 41 pp. 419-424.

Dungal, H. (1061) The special problem of stomach cancer in Iceland. J. Amer. med. Ass. 178 pp. 789-798.

Fridriksson, S. (1973) Lif og land, Vardi, Reykjavik.

Fridriksson, S. (1975) Surtsey, Butterworth, London.

Gudleifsson, B., and Gunnarsson, G.H. (1978) Hörgulkvillar i fodurkali. Radunautafundur, Agricultural Society and Agric. Res. Inst. Reykjavik, 3 pp. 174-178.

Gudmundsson, O., Thorsteinsson, Th., Arnalds, A., Palmason, F., Mundell, D. and Thorsteinsson, S.S. (1976) Preliminary report on mineral studies in grazing experiments. (A mimeograph) Agric. Res. Institute Reykjavik.

Gudmunsson, K.R. (1971) Clinical studies of multiple sclerosis in Iceland. Munksgaard, Köbenhavn pp. 78.

Gudmunsson, B. and Thorsteinsson, Th. (1976) Kobolt i islenzku grasi. Mimeographic report and Annual reports of the Inst. for Experimental Pathology, University of Iceland.

Helgadottir, A. and Palmason, F (1976) Ahrif kölkunar a grasvöxt, protein og steinefni i grasi. Mimeograph 7 Agric. Res. Inst., Reykjavik, pp. 29.

Helgadottir, A., Palmason, F. and Björnsson H. (1977) The effect of sulphur fertilization on hay yield and its influence on sulphur content of grass. J. Agric. Research in Iceland 9:2, pp. 3-21.

Johannesson, B. (1961) The utilization of phosphorus in pot experiments and field trials. Rit landbunadardeildar B6 pp. 37.

Larusson, Th. (1977) Starfsskyrslur. Arsit ræktunarfelags Nordurlands. 74 pp. 90.

Möller, P. (1972) Epidemiologic and genetic study of cleft lip and cleft palate in Iceland. Alabama J. Med. Sci. 9:2 pp. 119-136.

Olafsson, G., and Eiriksson, T. (1976) Heygædi a oþurrkasvædum 1976. Freyr, 21 pp. 480-482.

Palsson, P.A. and Grimsson, H. (1053) Demyelination in lambs from ewes which feed on seaweeds. Proc. Soc. exp. Biol. (N.Y.) 83 pp. 518-520.

Palmason, F. (1973) Rannsoknir a plöntunæringarefnum i nytjajurtum. Report of the Div. of Plant Science, Agric. Research Institue, Reykjavik pp. 35.

Palmason, F. (1972) Report of the Division of Plant Science, Agricultural Research Institute Reykjavik, p. 35.

Palmason, F. (1978) Personal Communications.

Rist, S. (1974) Efnarannsokn vatns 1973. Orkustofnun, Reykjavik.

Sigurdsson, S. and Thorsteinsson, Th. (1978) Krampadodi, bradadaudi og magnesiumskortur. Handbok bænda, Agricultural Society, Reykjavik.

Sigurjonsson, J. (1938) Um skjaldkirtilsjukdomar, einkum her a landi. Læknabladid 24:4 49-57.

...... (1040) Studies on the human thyroid in Iceland. Edda h.f., Reykjavik, pp. 130.

...... (1943) Diet and Health in Iceland. Rikisprentsmidjan Gutenberg, Reykjavik.

Sigvaldason, J. (1967) Rannsoknir a brennisteinsskorti i islenzkum tunum: III. Nokkrar athuganir a brennisteinsmagni i jardvegi. Arsrit Ræktunarfelags Nordurlands, 64, pp. 113-126.

Warren, H.V. (1959) Geology and multiple sclerosis. Nature 184, pp. 561.

World Health Statistics, WHO, Geneve, 1972-1977.

On the Relationship between the Contents of Trace Elements in Soils and Plants and the Cancer Incidence in Finland

Helvi Marjanen

INTRODUCTION

The statistics show that the cancer incidence in Finland is high compared with the international level. According to the latest statistics, from 1973, 249.1 males and 172.0 females per 100,000 inhabitants, suffered from cancer (Anon. 1976). According to Teppo et al. (1975), an average of 254.9 males and 169.7 females per 100,000 inhabitants suffered from cancer, and 191.8 males and 103.7 females died of cancer in the years 1966-70.

Clemmessen (1965) and Saxén & Hakama (1967) have classified factors associated with a high incidence of cancer, particularly stomach cancer. For instance among the soil factors, they mention acid soils and peatlands, and among the nutrient factors, a high consumption of cereals and a high zinc/copper-ratio. This investigation handles these matters more closely.

MATERIALS

The cancer figures are based on the statistical data of the Finnish Cancer Registry from 1961-1967, and the trace element analyses of the cultivated soils are on determinations made by Viljavuuspalvelu Oy from 1964-1970. A total of 20601 manganese and 42303 copper analyses were available in this investigation. The 97 grain samples collected from local experimental farms were analysed at the Isotope Laboratory of the Agricultural Research Centre.

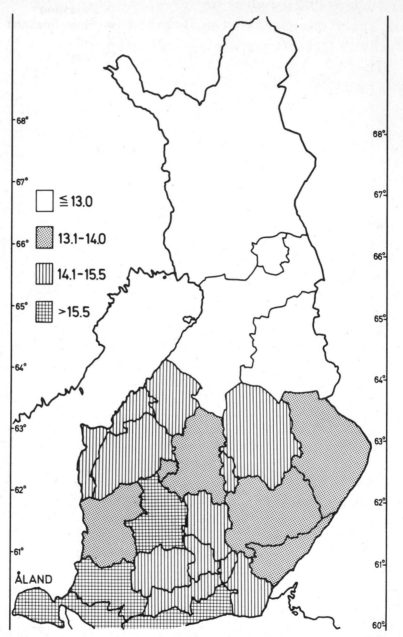

Figure 1. Female cancer age-adjusted incidence in 1961–70 per 1000 inhabitants.

150

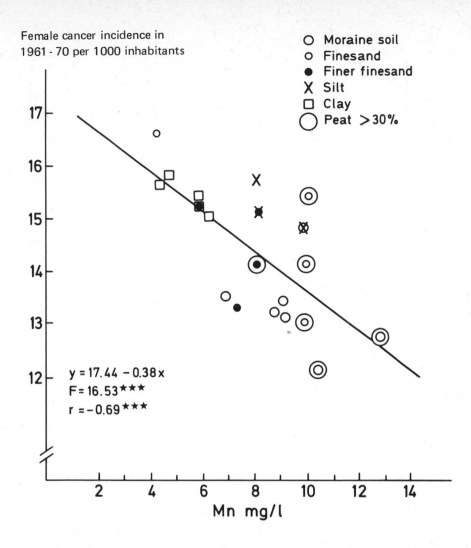

Average manganese contents in mineral soils in districts of agricultural extension centres 1964—70.

Figure 2. The relationship between the content of manganese in cultivated soil and the female cancer age-adjusted incidence.

RESULTS

Marjanen (1969) compared the cancer incidences in 179 parishes during the years 1961-1965 (5 years/per 1000 inhabitants), with the manganese contents in soil samples taken from cultivated mineral soils, which were determined by using 0.1 N magnesium sulphate. It could be seen that the greater the manganese content in the soil, the smaller the cancer incidence was in the parishes. In this calculation, it was impossible to take the age-adjustment into account.

The material was re-classified by combining the parishes into larger areas and analysing the relationship between easily soluble manganese and the cancer incidence, taking the age-adjustment for females and males separately into consideration. The age-adjustment was calculated in the manner proposed by Hakama (1970), in which the whole country's average was used as a standard.

Fig. 1 shows the relative cancer incidence among women in 1961-67 per 1000 inhabitants in various areas of the agricultural centres, taking the age-adjustment into consideration, and Fig. 2 shows the results of the relationship calculated between the average contents of easily soluble manganese in the mineral soils and the cancer incidence among women. Although the areas were large and the soil types varied greatly, the female cancer incidence decreased highly significantly by increasing amounts of easily soluble manganese in mineral soils. Fig. 3 shows the average pH of the surface soil samples during 1966-70 and the main soil types in the various areas of the agricultural centres. The heavily limed clay soil areas in South and South-Western Finland form a group, where the cancer incidence is high. In the coarse finesand area (Åland), where the manganese is low, there is a high cancer incidence. The moraine soil areas in Eastern and Northern Finland form a group where the cancer incidence is lower. In peat soil areas, the humus content of mineral soils is higher than elsewhere and the pH is usually lower.

Fig. 4 shows the incidence of cancer among males during 1961-67 per 1000 inhabitants, taking the age-adjustment into consideration. The areas of Northern Karjala and Kuopio differ

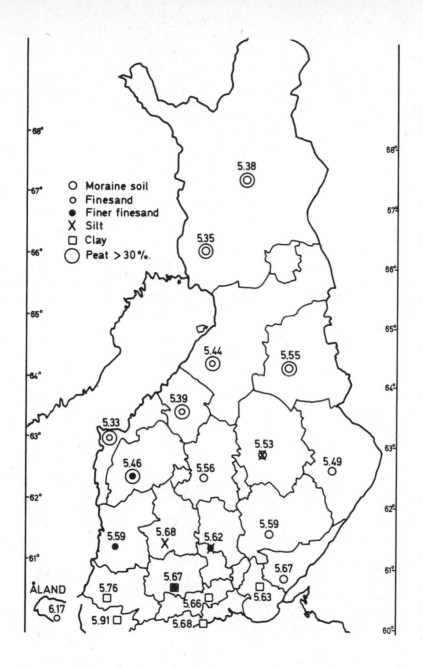

Figure 3. The average pH of surface soil samples during 1966–70 and the main soil types in various areas of agricultural extension centres.

153

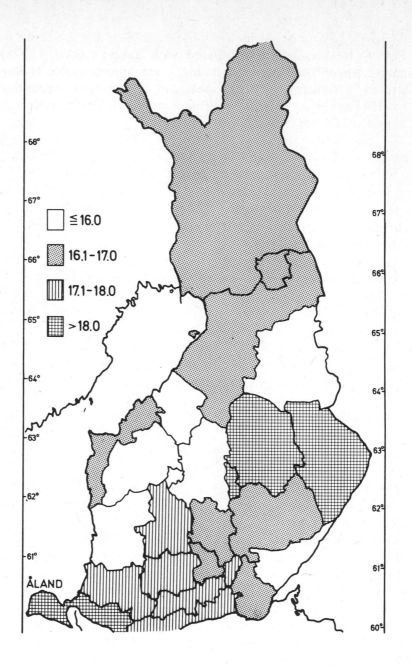

Figure 4. Male cancer age-adjusted incidence in 1960–70 per 1000 inhabitants.

154

decisively from the incidence among females that is shown in Fig. 1. If this chart is compared with Teppo's et al. (1975) chart, where the lung cancer incidence among males is illustrated, a similarity in these areas can be observed. According to Heinonen et al. (1972), smoking is greater in Northern Karjala than it is in Western Finland.

It has been found, in many connections, that smoking increases the risk of lung cancer (Hakama 1970). It can be assumed that smoking has increased incidences in the areas of Kuopio and Northern Karjala and therefore, by using the lung cancer averages, the cancer incidence of the two areas were corrected. When this was done, the correlation (Fig. 5) was fairly significant ($F = 4.49^X$).

The study was continued by comparing the content of acid soluble copper in the soil and the age-adjusted cancer incidence in females. Fig. 6 indicates this correlation. The copper was determined from ash, by using 2 N hydrochloric acid as an extraction liquid.

Fig. 7 shows a study made on the relationship between the manganese/copper-ratio in the cultivated soils and the age-adjusted cancer incidence in females in the agricultural centre areas. When the ratio is low, the cancer incidence is high.

According to Clemmessen (1965) and Saxén & Hakama (1967), the cancer incidence is raised by a high zinc/copper-ratio. On account of the scarce zinc determination, it was not possible to study the zinc/copper-ratio on the basis of soil analyses. Because an abundant consumption of grain was mentioned as a risk factor, the crop samples were therefore studied. Wheat samples (spring and winter wheat) were requested from farms where local trials were arranged. An inquiry was also made into the diseases that had occurred on the farms during the last 50-100 years; for instance, how many cases of cancer, heart diseases, diabetes, liver trouble, etc. there had been. Samples and responses were obtained from 97 farms.

It was found that, among these 97 farms, there were only 25 farms (25.8%), whose inhabitants had suffered no serious illnesses during the past 50-100 years. The grain analyses from those farms are shown in Table 1. It was interesting to note that in every farm where no cancer cases have occurred, there

155

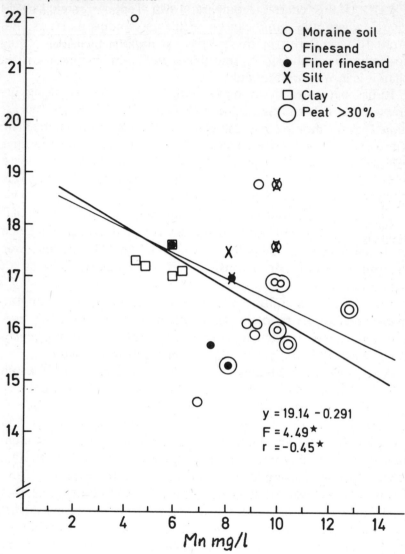

Average manganese contents in mineral soils in districts of agricultural extension centres 1964—70.

Figure 5. Relationship between the content of manganese in cultivated soil and the male cancer age-adjusted incidence.

Table 1. Analyses of trace elements from grain samples taken in 1969 from farms where no cases of cancer, heart, liver, kidney or other diseases have occurred for 50—100 years.

			mg/kg in dry matter			
Parish	Plant	Soil type	Mn	Fe	Cu	Zn
Tuusula	sw	Muddy clay	44	57.4	5.60	43.8
Askola	sw	Sandy clay	47	35.6	5.53	39.6
Jämsänkoski	sw	Finer finesand	28	24.0	4.15	25.1
Ruotsinpyhtää	sw	Sandy clay	45	49.1	4.82	35.9
Honkajärvi	sw	Finesand	51	32.6	4.74	32.3
Ruovesi	sw	Peat	40	30.2	6.30	32.3
Ikaalinen	ww	Sandy clay	40	37.9	6.14	37.3
Valkeala	sw	Sandy clay	55	27.4	5.04	30.1
Joroinen	sw	Moraine soil	47	36.1	6.41	36.7
Rääkkylä	sw	Moraine soil	76	49.8	6.74	47.2
— » —	sw	Finer finesand	84	44.2	6.96	44.7
Vehkalahti			66	36.2	4.71	33.3
Lapinlahti	sw	Moraine soil	62	35.5	5.53	40.4
Nurmo	ww	Moraine soil	98	37.4	3.91	34.6
Hollola	ww	Finer finesand	29	24.8	4.76	26.5
Metsämaa	ww	Muddy clay	37	26.2	6.77	30.1
Snappertuna	sw	Sandy clay	43	26.6	6.37	30.4
Brändö	sw	Moraine clay	38	18.8	5.58	33.5
Laihia	ww	Sandy clay	37	26.3	6.12	34.7
Töysä	ww	Silt	32	37.0	3.66	29.6
Lapinjärvi	sw	Mud	55	38.2	4.81	30.1
Loimaa	sw	Sandy clay	44	39.7	6.05	38.7
Isokyrö	sw	Muddy clay	48	41.8	5.64	37.9
Pyhtää	ww		41	31.2	5.94	34.3
Lapinjärvi	sw	Silty clay	49	32.9	6.13	42.3
n. 25		$\bar{x}$	49.4	35.1	5.54	35.3

sw = spring wheat, ww = winter wheat

was a higher amount of manganese than zinc in the cereal. The average content of manganese was 14.1 mg/kg in dry matter, greater than the zinc's average content, and the iron and zinc contents between themselves were equal.

157

Table 2. Analyses of trace elements from grain samples taken in 1969 from farms where two or more cases of cancer have occurred.

Parish	Plant	Soil type	mg/kg in dry matter Mn	Fe	Cu	Zn	Number of cancer cases
Eräjärvi	ww	Moraine soil	29	25.6	4.65	46.0	4
Houtskari	ww	Sandy clay	22	27.5	6.39	36.4	2
Ruotsinpyhtää	sw	Sandy clay	37	39.4	5.59	40.6	2
Kumlinge	sw	Sandy clay	35	31.3	5.67	40.8	2
Mustasaari	sw	Muddy clay	54	26.7	5.97	41.0	2
Kumlinge	sw	Sandy clay	35	24.2	5.29	41.2	2
Sottunga	r	Sandy clay	31	26.6	5.85	31.9	2
Kumlinge	sw	Sandy clay	18	23.7	5.26	35.0	2
n. 7		$\bar{x}$	33.1	28.5	5.72	38.1	
n. 6		$\bar{x}$	29.7	28.8	5.68	37.7	

sw = spring wheat, ww = winter wheat, r = rye

Table 2 shows the grain analyses from those farms where two or more inhabitants had suffered from cancer. There was a total of 8 farms (8.2%) among the material. On the farm where four cases of cancer had occurred, the zinc content of the grain was 16 mg/kg in dry matter, greater than the manganese content. In relation to the zinc content, the iron content was also low. On examining the cereals of farms with two cases of cancer, only one had a manganese content greater than the zinc content. Also, iron was lower than zinc. The amount of copper on these farms was a trifle more than on the "healthy" farms, but there was no decisive difference in the copper content. Farms with only one case of cancer and those which had suffered other illnesses were therefore excluded from these examinations.

DISCUSSION

Most of the cultivated soils in Finland, i.e. 28.7%, fell into the class of pH 5.5-5.8 in 1972. A lower class (pH 5.2-5.5) pre-

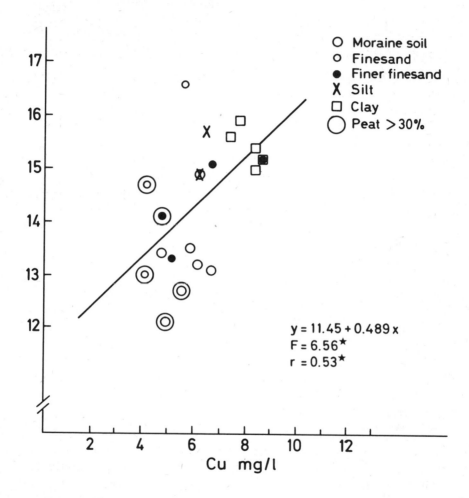

Female cancer incidence in
1961-67 per 1000 inhabitants

Average copper contents in mineral soils in districts of agricultural extension
centres 1964—70.

*Figure 6. Relationship between the content of copper in cultivated soil and
the female cancer age-adjusted incidence.*

Female cancer incidence in
1961-67 per 1000 inhabitants.

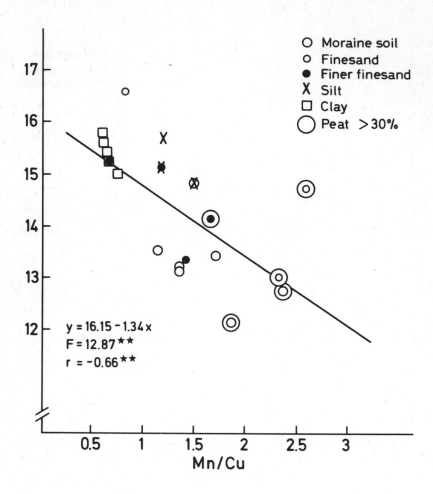

Manganese/copper-ratio in mineral soils

Figure 7. Managenese/copper-ratio of mineral soils and the female cancer age-adjusted incidence.

160

vailed in Northern Finland. The soils pH 5.8-6.1, belonged mostly to the farming areas of Western Finland. The soils pH 6.1-6.4, prevailed in Åland and the islands (Kurki 1972), where the cancer incidence is the highest.

Many researchers have found, as White et al. (1970) did, that the amount of manganese in a plant is directly proportional to the acidity of the soil. In many experiments, liming the soils that have a pH 6.5 or above, caused a substantial reduction in the amount of manganese in the plants.

In Finland, the contents of manganese in the soils have steadily declined. The amount of manganese in cattle manure per hectare of ploughland, decreased in the 1960s by 20%. In the 1970s, almost all the manganese in compound fertilizers was applied to potato and root crop lands, which account for 3% of the ploughland (Valmari & Marjanen 1976). In Finland, it can be imagined that where the contents of easily soluble manganese in the soil are high, the manganese contents in the plants are also high. High zinc concentrations have also been found to inhibit the uptake of manganese, for instance in rice (Ishisuka & Ando 1968). The amounts of manganese in cereals have continuously declined in the grain-growing areas in Sourthern Finland. Also, zinc contents have increased in relation to the contents of manganese and iron.

Laker (1976) found that the phosphorus fertilization increased the uptake of zinc in maize. In Finland, numerous compound fertilizers contain 15% to 24% of P_2O_5, and therefore the amount of phosphorus given in fertilizers per hectare is higher than in other Scandinavian countries (Anon. 1977). In Finland, large amounts of phosphorus may cause higher zinc contents in plants and grains than in other countries where less phosphorus is used. The soils in Finland are also relatively low in boron. According to Parks et al. (1944), this tends to increase the amount of zinc in plants.

Finland belongs to a low selenium region. According to Oksanen & Sandholm (1970), the contents of selenium in cereals vary from 0.002-0.084 mg/kg in dry matter.

Trace elements, manganese, selenium, copper and zinc have recently been an object of interest among cancer researchers. Their significance in the metabolism of people and animals has been investigated. According to Warburg (1956), the cancer cells characteristics are that the respiration is damaged and the formation of lactic acid increases, until almost half of the cells ATP energy is produced under anaerobic conditions. Olson (1966) has analysed the function of ubiquinone, i.e. the co-enzyme Q, which is necessary to the respiratory chain of the cell in animals, and Trelfall (1971) has done the same with plants. According to Edwin et al. (1961) and Green et al. (1961), selenium in the nutrition increases the concentration of ubiquinones in the same why as alpha-tocopherol does, and a biosynthetic relationship seems to exist between them. A deficiency in vitamin E and selenium reduces the level of ubiquinone, i.e. co-enzyme Q, in the tissues of rats and rabbits. On the basis of Olson's and Trelfall's studies, Frost (1972) provides a clarification of how manganese and selenium act in the synthesis of ubiquinone in connection with vitamin B_{12} and methionine.

If manganese and selenium form a functional pair, we can understand Burch's et al. (1975) study, where a manganese deficiency in pigs caused a reduction in the amount of selenium in tissues, but not in the kidneys. A disturbance in this mechanism is also caused by excess zinc. According to Schrauzer (1977), zinc and other minerals in normal food, prevent the uptake of selenium from nutrition. Zinc has been found to reduce the action of cytochrome C-oxidase in the respiratory chain (Duncan et al. 1953). A deficiency in either selenium or manganese, as well as an excess of zinc, weakens the function of the respiratory chain.

Can we now assume that a deficiency of manganese and selenium, as well as an abundance of zinc, has a carcinogenic effect? The abundance of zinc in Finnish nutrition may prevent the absorption of selenium, and a shortage of manganese in many areas may reduce the utilization of selenium in the cells.

SUMMARY

Marjanen (1969) has found that with an increase in the amount of soluble manganese in mineral soils, the cancer incidence decreases highly significantly. The same phenomenon was studied separately for females and males, taking the age-adjustment into consideration in different agricultural extension centres. It was found that with an increase in the content of manganese, the cancer incidence among females declined highly significantly ($F = 16.53^{XXX}$). For males a fairly significant difference was obtained ($F = 4.49^X$), when the national lung cancer averages were used in the areas of Northern-Karjala and Kuopio.

A fairly significant difference was obtained between the contents of copper in cultivated mineral soils and the cancer incidence among females, when the age-adjustment was taken into consideration. It was found that with an increase in the content of copper, the cancer incidence among females increased ($F = 6.56^X$).

A study of the manganese/copper-ratio in mineral soils showed that, when the ratio declined, the cancer incidence in females increased significantly ($F = 12.87^{XX}$).

The grain samples were studied from 97 farms. On the farms (25.8%) where no serious illnesses had occurred for 50-100 years, there was, on an average, 14.1 mg/kg more of manganese than zinc in the cereals, and the contents of iron and zinc in the grain were equal. On farms (8.2%) where two or more cases of cancer had occurred, the amount of zinc in the grain was higher than manganese and the amount of iron was low, in relation to zinc.

REFERENCES

Anon. 1976. Cancer incidence in Finland 1973. Finnish Cancer Registry — The Institute for Statistical and Epidemiological Cancer Research, XVIII/ 1973. Helsinki 28 p.

- 1977. Kemira Oy Vuosikertomus 1976. Helsinki 36 p.

Beer, K. 1968. (Effect of liming on dynamics of manganese in different soils of the German Democratic Republic, and utilization of manganese by plants.) Agrokhimiya, No. 7, 83-84. (Ref. Manganese in plant nutrition 1974-1966. C.A.B. N:o 1723, 7.)

Burch, R.E., R.W. William, H.K.J. Hahn, M.M. Jetton, & J.F. Sullivan, 1975. Tissue trace element and entzyme content in pigs fed a low manganese diet. 1. A relationship between manganese and selenium. J. of lab. and clin. med., 86 (1), 132-139. Nutr. Abstr. and Rev. 1976, 46, 11: 984, 8954.

Chaudhry, F.M., & J.F. Loneragan. 1972. Zinc absorption by wheat seedlings and the nature of its inhibition by alkaline earth cations. J. exp. Bot., 23 (75), 552-560.

Chaudhry, F.M., M. Sharif, A. Latif, & R.H. Gureshi, 1973. Zinc-copper antagonism in the nutrition of rice (Oryza sativa L.). Plant and soil, 38 (3), 573-580.

Clemmessen, J. 1965. Statistical studies in malignant neoplasms. Copenhagen 543 p.

Duncan, G.D., L.F. Gray, L.J. Daniel, 1953. Effect of zinc on cytochrome oxidase activity. Proc. Soc. exp. Biol. (N.Y.), 83: 625-627. (Ref. Petering, H.G. 1974.)

Edwin, E.E., A.T. Diplock, J. Bunyan, & J. Green, 1961. Studies on vitamin E. The distribution of vitamin E in the rat and the effect of α-tocopherol and dietary selenium on ubiquinone and ubichromenol in tissues. Biochem.J, 79:91-105.

Elliot, J.M., 1969. Effect of applied manganese, sulphur and phosphorus on the manganese content of oats and flue-cured tobacco. Canad. J. Soil Sci., 49, 227-285.

Frost, D.V., 1972. The two faces of selenium — can selenophobia be cured? CRC Critical Reviews in toxicology, 1, 4, 467-514.

Ghonein, M.F., M.H. El-Gibaly & H.G. Hassanin, 1974. The status of manganese in the soil and rice plants under different water systems and fertilizer applications. Plant and soil, 41 (2), 313-324.

Green, J., A.T. Diplock, J. Bunyan & E.E. Edwin, 1961. Studies on vitamin E. Vitamin E, ubiquinone and ubichromenol in the rabbit. Biochem. J., 79, 108-111.

Haag, H.P., & E.J.R. Sarruge, 1967. Uptake of zinc by detached roots of young coffee trees (Coffea arabica L. variety Novo Mundo). Fertilite, 29, 13-22.

Hakama, M., 1970. Age-adjustment of incidence rates in cancer epidemiology. Acta path. microbio. scand., Suppl. 213, 1-46.

Heinonen, O.P., H. Poppius, M. Tamminen & A. Aromaa, 1972. Tupakointi ja kuolleisuus suomalaisessa väestössä. Duodecim, 88, 1239.

Ishisuka, Y. & T. Ando, 1968. Interaction between manganese and zinc in growth of rice plants. Soil Sci. Pl. Nutr., 14, 201-206.

Kmet, J. & E. Mahboubi, 1972. Esophageal cancer in the Caspian littoral of Iran: Initial studies. Detailed studies of geographical pathology are opening new vistas in cancer epidemiology. Science, 175, 4024, 846-853.

Kurki, M. Suomen peltojen viljavuudesta, II. Viljavuuspalvelu Oy. p. 182. Helsinki.

Laker, M.C., 1967. (Uptake of zinc and phosphorus by plants from a sandy soil.) S. Afr. J. agric. sci., 10, 323-330. (Ref. C.A.B. N:o 1728,23.)

164

Lopez, P.L. & E.R. Graham, 1973. Labile pool and plant uptake of micro-nutrients, II. Uptake of Mn, Fe and Zn by Ladino clover (Trifolium repens) and its relation to soil labile pools. Soil science, 115 (5), 380-389.

Maas, E.V., D.P. Moore & B.J. Mason, 1968. Manganese absorption by excised barley roots. Pl. Physiol., Lancaster 43, 527-530.

Marjanen, H., 1969. Possible causal relationship between the easily soluble amount of manganese on arable mineral soil and susceptibility to cancer in Finland. Ann. agric. Fenn., 8, 326-334.

Misra, S.G. & P.C. Mishra, 1968. Response of (barley plants to added manganese.) Boln Inst. nac. Invest. agron., Madr. 28, 161-171. (Ref. C.A.B. N:o 1723, 6.)

Oksanen, H.E. & M. Sandholm, 1970. The selenium content of Finnish forage crops. Maat. tiet. Aikak., 41, 4, 250-253.

Olson, R.E., 1966. Biosynthesis of ubiquinones in animals. Vitamins and hormones, 24, 551-574.

Parks, R.Q., C.B. Lyon & S.L. Hood, 1944. Some effects of boron supply on the chemical composition of tomato leaflets. Plant physiol., 19, 404-419.

Petering, H.G., 1974. Effect of cadmium and lead on copper and zinc metabolism. Trace element metabolism in animals - 2. Baltimore 1974, 311-325.

Rose, E.F., 1968. The effects of soil and diet on disease. Cancer, 28, 2390-92.

Saxén, E.A. & M. Hakama, 1967. The different incidence of gastric cancer all over the world and possible reasons for this difference. Ninth Intern. Cancer Congr. U.I.C.C., 10, 49-55.

Schrauzer, G.N., 1977. Trace elements, nutrition and cancer: Perspectives of prevention. IABS Conf. — Bioinorganic and nutritional aspects of cancer. Univ. of Calif., Jan. 2-5, at La Jolla.

Teppo, L., M. Hakama, T. Hakulinen, M. Lehtonen & E. Saxén, 1975. Cancer in Finland 1953-1970: Incidence, mortality, prevalence. Acta. path. microbio. scand. Section A, 1975. Suppl. No, 252. Copenhagen 79 p.

Threlfall, D.R., 1971. The biosynthesis of vitamin E and K and related compounds. Vitamins and hormones, 29, 153-200.

Tromp, S.W. & J.C. Diehl, 1955. A statistical study of the possible relationship between cancer of the stomach and soil. Brit. J. Cancer, 9, 3, 350-357.

Wallace, A., S.M. Sufi & E.M. Romney, 1970. Regulation of heavy metal uptake and responses in plants. In: Recent Advances in plant nutrition. Proceedings 6th International Colloquium on plants Analysis and Fertilizer Problems. Tel Aviv.

Valmari, M. & H. Marjanen, 1976. Viljelysmaiden helppoliukoisen mangaanin vähentymisestä. Maatalouden tutkimuskeskus, paikalliskoetoimiston tiedote, No. 5, 11-28.

Warburg, O., 1956. On the origin of cancer cells. Science, 123, 309-314.

White, R.P., E.C. Doll & J.R. Melton, 1970. Growth and manganese uptake by potatoes as related to liming and acidity of fertilizer bands. Proc. Soil Sci. Soc. Ann. 34, 268-271.

Finnish Research Project on Mineral Elements in Soils, Plants and Foodstuffs

Esko Saari

INTRODUCTION

During the last few years the national health problems have been a subject of lively discussion in Finland. Special attention has been paid to the quality of foodstuffs and their raw materials with regard to the effect of their mineral element content on human health. The nature of the changes that have occurred in the quality of our food is also the subject of investigation. The mineral content of foodstuffs can be affected by many factors, and in order to find practical solutions to various problems we ought to know for example:

- how the mineral content of cereal products depends on the properties of soil,
- to what extent mineral elements can be affected by fertilizing technology,
- the extent of the transition of toxic elements of the soil into plants,
- the mineral element content of foodstuffs,
- the significane of the effect of industrial processing on the mineral element content of foodstuffs.

These are some of the problems for which we expected to find a solution in the research project on mineral elements which was started in Finland three years ago and which is now near completion. The project has been devided into two parts: 'soil

167

and plants' and 'foodstuffs'. This has been a joint research project in which the Institute of Food Chemistry and Technology of Helsinki University has collected the food samples, the Agricultural Research Centre has analyzed the grass samples and the corresponding soils, and Kemira Oy has analyzed the cereal and food samples.

The Agricultural Research Centre is a scientific institution subordinated to the Ministry of Agriculture and Forestry, and it carries out research and experiments with the object of promoting and developing various fields of agriculture. Kemira Oy is the largest state-owned chemical company in Finland, and its main line is the production of fertilizers and industrial and agricultural chemicals.

The total budget of this project amounts to approximately 3 million Fmk; it has been financed by those taking part in this research, with additional financial support from the Finnish Academy.

The main objective of the project 'soil and plants' is to get a general view on the mineral content of the arable soils, to investigate the correlation between the mineral element content of soil and crop, to get a general idea of the mineral alement content of animal feed, to investigate the effect of fertilizing technology on the mineral element content of plants, and to trace the transition of toxic heavy metals into plants. In the course of this project 4000 soil samples and 4500 plant samples were analyzed, with a total amount of 200,000 determinations. The results of this research project will be published in the series *Acta Agriculturae Scandinavia* at the end of this year. The list of contents of this publication is enclosed, see References.

The results reveal e.g. that Mg, B, and Cu, as applied to the soil in addition to NKP-fertilizers, seem to give a perfect crop of grain. The content of some mineral elements (F, Se, Mo, Co, and Cr) in Finnish cereals are relatively low. The harmful elements Hg, Pb, and As do not transfer easily into grains through the soil, with the exception of Cd.

PROJECT 'FOODSTUFFS'

The analytical work of this project was completed in January 1978. The project was carried out in five successive stages; first cereals and cereal products were analyzed, secondly meat and meat products, thirdly potato and other vegetables, then milk and milk products, and finally prepared foods and diets. The total amount of samples was approximately 2000, and 25 elements were determined from each sample, which makes a total of 50,000 determinations. The element content of the samples ranged widely, from the highest content of one per cent to the lowest content of one millionth per cent. The primary goal was to determine the nutritionally essential elements N, Mg, P, S, K, Ca, Cr, Mn, Fe, Co, Cu, Zn, Se and Mo. Furthermore, some elements were determined which are either essential or whose content in foodstuffs is regularly high, viz. B, F, Si, Al, Ni, Br, and Rb. The toxic elements As, Cd, Hg, and Pb were also determined.

The results of this research project now completed form a good basis for nutritional research and advisory work. It is now possible to estimate whether there is in man's nutritional conditions any deficiency that could be compensated by proper fertilizing technique or by further processing of food products. These results will also be published in the series *Acta Agriculturae Scandinavia*. The list of contents of this publication is enclosed, see Table 1.

ANALYTICAL METHODS

The analysis of foodstuff samples was the biggest problem. The decisive factors in the choice of an analytical scheme were, in the first place, the equipment and personnel available, and secondly the unusually large quantity of elements and their concentrations. To carry out the analytical work with a minimum of cost, instrumental methods were chosen which could be applied to as many elements as possible. This scheme was somewhat generalized, so that as many samples as possible could be determined after similar preparation. Preference was given to flame atomic absorption. It was used for the determination of Mg, Al, K, Ca, Mn, Fe, Cu, Zn, and Rb. Flameless atomic absorption was used in the determination of Cr, Co, Ni, Cd, Hg, and Pb, because their concentrations were too low for flame atomic absorption. Selenium was determined by hydride generation using quartz tube atomizer and H_2O_2-flame. Bromine was determined by x-ray fluorescence. Individual chemical methods were used to determine each of the following elements: B, N, F, Si, P, S, As, and Mo.

The reliability of the analytical results was tested by the NBS-standards: No. 1571 'orchard leaves' and No. 1577 'bovine liver', and the test results were in full agreement with the results given by us.

JOINT-VENTURE POSSIBILITIES

The project, with a total duration of four years, was completed in January 1978 as far as the analytical part of it is concerned. In the course of the last three years the Oulu Research Laboratory of Kemira Oy has reached a very high level of skills in the determination of both minor and especially trace elements from different kinds of biological samples. Therefore we wish to make it known that, as far as determinations of minor and trace elements from biological samples are concerned, our know-how, laboratory staff, and equipment are available if a decision about starting joint-venture projects is made at this symposium or at a later date.

Table 1. Mineral element composition of Finnish foods

1. Introduction.
2. Analytical methods.
3. Annual variation of the mineral element composition in cereal grains.
4. Mineral element composition of flours and bakery products.
5. Mineral element composition of meat and fish, and their industrial products.
6. Mineral element composition of vegetables, fruit, berries and mushrooms.
7. Mineral element composition of dairy products and eggs.
8. Mineral element composition of beverages and confectioneries.
9. Mineral element composition of industrial foods and baby formulae.
10. Mineral element composition of average total diets.

REFERENCES

1. Sippola, Jouko, and Tauno Tares. The soluble content of mineral elements in cultivated Finnish soils.
2. Kähäri, Jorma, and Helena Nissinen. The mineral element contents of timothy (Phleum pratense L.) in Finland. I. The elements: calcium, magnesium, phosphorus, potassium, chromium, cobalt, copper, iron, manganese, sodium, and zinc.
3. Paasikallio, Arja. The mineral element contents of timothy (Phleum pratense L.) in Finland . II. The Elements: aluminum, boron, molybdenum, strontium, lead, and nickel.
4. Jaakkola, Antti, and Paula Vogt. The effect of mineral elements added to Finnish soils on the mineral contents of cereal, potato, and hay crops. II. The elements: aluminium, boron, molybdenum, strontium, copper, iron, manganese, sodium, and zinc.
5. Vogt, Paula, and Antti Jaakkola. The effect of mineral elements added to Finnish soils on the mineral contents of cereal, potato, and hay crops. II. The elements: aluminium, boron, molbybdenum, strontium, chromium, cobalt, lead, and nickel.
6. Syvälahti, Jorma, and Johan Korkman. The effect of applied mineral elements on the mineral content and yield of cereals and potato in Finland.
7. Tares, Tauno, and Jouko Sippola. Changes in pH, in electrical conductivity and in the extractable amounts of mineral elements in soil, and the utilization and losses of the elements in some field experiments.

Gaucher's Disease in Sweden and Its Hypothetical Dependence on Metal Anomalies in the Soil

P-O. Hillborg

Gaucher's Disease (GD) is a lipidosis, a disorder of the lipid metabolism depending on a deficiency of an enzyme, β-glucosidase. This enzyme contributes to the decomposition of certain lipids, cerebrosides. Cerebroside is a constituent of nerve cells, necessary for their biological functions. The walls of red blood corpuscles also contain cerebroside. The patient with Gaucher's Disease can build up cerebroside and form the red blood corpuscles, but when these, after a life span of about 3 weeks, are to be destroyed and removed from the body, the cerebroside molecule can not be broken down. Therefore the lipid is retained and stored in different organs. Normally the red blood corpuscles are destroyed in the spleen, and so the greatest amount of cerebroside is stored in this organ.

Because of this, the first symptom of GD is an enlargement of the spleen, which often begins as early as the first year of life and proceeds rapidly. The heaviest spleen reported in a patient with GD had a weight of 12 kg. That is 100 times the weight of a normal spleen.

Cerebroside is stored in the bone marrow too and obstructs the normal formation of blood cells. A certain amount of lipid accumulates in the arterial walls of the brain and causes a thickening of these walls with a diminished oxygen and nutritive support of the nerve cells. This is the probable cause of the neurological symptoms that appear in some of the GD patients (1).

The author has made a survey of the occurrence of GD in all Sweden and found 55 cases. The distribution is seen in Fig. 1, in which every patient is marked with a black spot. The material includes: one "Norrbotten group" with 16 patients in 11 families, one "Västerbotten group" with 20 patients in 16 families, and one "southern group" with 19 patients in 15 families.

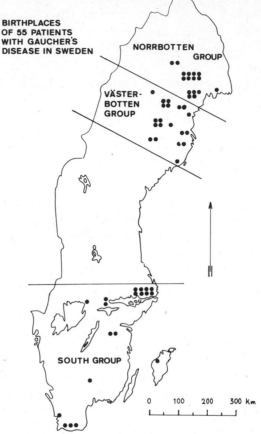

The area of Sweden in which the 36 patients of the "Norrbotten group" and the "Västerbotten group" together have their origin is about the same size as the area of the "southern group". Thus it seems as if GD were twice as common in the north of Sweden as in the south. However, in the period in which the 55 patients with GD were born, the population of the Norrbotten and the Västerbotten counties together was about 350,000 individuals, compared with aproximately 4.5 millions of the 9 counties forming the area of the "southern group". Taking this into consideration it appears that *the incidence of GD is 13 times higher in northern Sweden than in southern.*

Let us discuss some different explanations of this unusually high incidence. Gaucher's Disease is inherited with an auto- somal, recessive gene. Fig. 2 a shows how this gene might have been propagated in one family through five successive gene- rations. It is assumed that the GD gene does not occur in any other family in the same area. Furthermore, the assumption is made that the GD gene has been created by a mutation in a germinal cell of the man in generation I, marked with a dotted quadrangle. The son of this man, in generation II, is the first carrier of the GD gene, the first GD heterozygote.

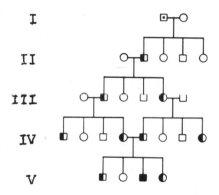

The two married first cousins in generation IV are the parents of the first patient with GD in that family. If no cousin mar- riage had occurred in this generation, the GD gene would not have manifested itself in the disease in generation V, but in later generations, possibly much later generations. It is impor- tant to keep it in mind that if a gene of recessive type is created in an individual living in a certain geographical area, *it will take at least 4 generations or about 100 years until the first individual with the manifest disease is born in that family*. At that time it might be the case that most members of the family have moved to other districts of the country.

If the incidence of a disease is high in a certain geographical area, there is, as a matter of fact, a possibility that the respon- sible gene was created by a mutation 100 years or several hun- dred years ago in quite another part of the country.

Of importance for the discussion is the fact that in such districts *where the rate of marriages between near relatives is high, the incidence of recessive diseases existing in the district is also high*. In many parts of the Norrbotten and Västerbotten counties the rate of such cousin marriages has been unusually high during several hundred years, but has diminished remarkably during the 20th century, because of an extensive migration of people. *This high degree of in-breeding in the north of Sweden is perhaps the only necessary explanation of the high incidence of GD* - but in the eyes of some genetician or some statistician it might possibly not be sufficient. Perhaps another contributory factor is demanded. *Hypothetically it could be an abnormally high mutation rate in one or several regions from which the GD families derive their origin*.

Normally mutations are very rare events, but if they were much more common, the theoretical situation in Fig. 2 b would

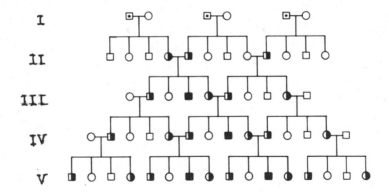

be established. Here are shown 3 different families in the same region, hit by the same mutation to GD. It is evident that the disease appears earlier and spreads faster in this group than in the solitary family of Fig. 2 a. A very high mutation rate, caused by some environmental factor, would be a much more effective means of raising the incidence of GD in the population than a high degree of in-breeding solely.

It is indeed very difficult to answer the question whether

environmental pollutants or other exogenous agents might be genetically hazardous to man (2), and the author has neither the capacity nor the ambition to solve this problem but only wants to enrich the discussion with some aspects of this material of GD in Sweden.

In order to discover the places where the GD ancestors of the "Norrbotten group" lived 5 generations ago, I went to the parish records and found the conditions seen in Fig. 3. Of the 176 forefathers in this "generation of the grandparents' grandparents", 96 lived in the little village of Överkalix at the Kalix river. My interest was then directed to Överkalix as the district where the GD mutation could possibly have taken place, possibly in several different families.

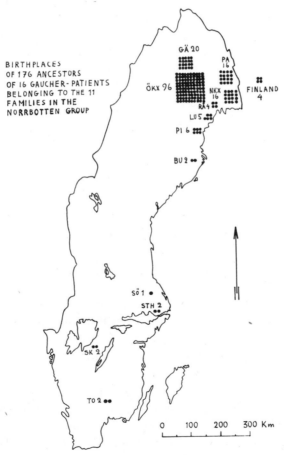

BIRTHPLACES
OF 176 ANCESTORS
OF 16 GAUCHER-PATIENTS
BELONGING TO THE 11
FAMILIES IN THE
NORRBOTTEN GROUP

GÄ 20
PA 16
ÖKX 96
NKX 16
FINLAND 4
RA 4
LU 5
PI 6
BU 2
SÖ 1
STH 2
SK 2
TO 2

0   100   200   300 Km

Since the parish records of Överkalix have been very thoroughly written up and well preserved ever since the end of the 17the country, it proved to be possible to continue the genealogical investigation 7 generations further back, resulting in the pedigree shown in Fig. 4. The figure shows that in the 11 fa-

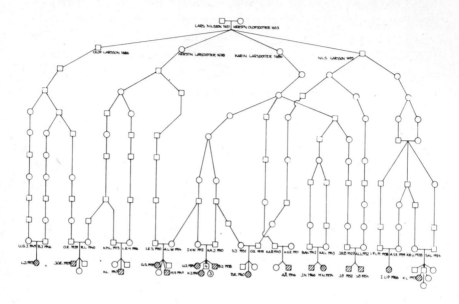

milies of the "Norrbotten group" all 22 parents except one have a common pair of ancestors, Lars Nilsson born in 1651 and his wife, Kerstin Olofsdotter born in 1653, both of them in Överkalix. The pedigree makes it much more probable that the GD gene has been propagated from Lars Nilsson or his wife through 12 generations to the GD patients of today than that the GD mutation appeared for the first time in the "generation of the grandparents' grandparents" about 100 years ago. It seems plausible that the mutation was created in Lars Nilsson or his wife or in one of their earlier forefathers, perhaps in some immigrant to Överkalix from the coast or from the south.

In the "Västerbotten group" the 256 ancestors in the "generation of the grandparents' grandparents" form 7 different large groups (Fig. 5), who lived in the districts of PI (Piteå), AJ (Arvidsjaur), MA (Malå), SK (Skellefteå), BU (Burträsk) and so on. Here the places of origin of the GD families are widespread,

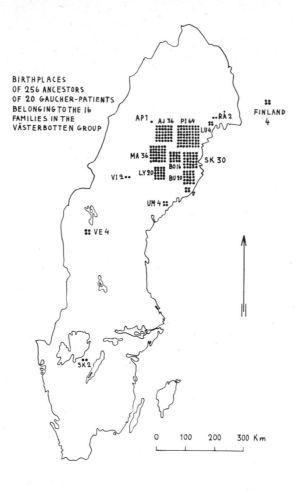

BIRTHPLACES
OF 256 ANCESTORS
OF 20 GAUCHER-PATIENTS
BELONGING TO THE 16
FAMILIES IN THE
VÄSTERBOTTEN GROUP

FINLAND
4

but on continuing the investigation one finds that several of the ancestors in Piteå, Arvidsjaur and Malå, earlier came from Skellefteå and Burträsk. *Therefore it is likely that the original mutation, responsible for the spreading of GD in the Västerbotten county, once took place in the Skellefteå-Burträsk district.* Possibly some emigrant from this area implanted the gene in Överkalix, where it might have spread because of a high degree of in-breeding.

The "southern group" contains 19 patients in 15 families. Only 10 of these families have been investigated in this respect.

179

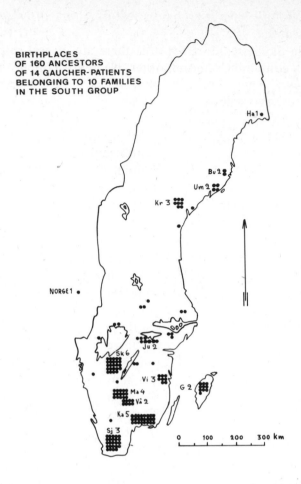

BIRTHPLACES
OF 160 ANCESTORS
OF 14 GAUCHER-PATIENTS
BELONGING TO 10 FAMILIES
IN THE SOUTH GROUP

In the 10 families there are 20 GD parents. Fig. 6 shows the 160 ancestors in the "generation of the grandparents' grandparents" marked with black dots. The symbol Sk 6 at the top of a 24 dot cluster means that 24 persons living in the Skara district are the ancestors of 6 GD parents. If we hope to find one common forefather to all GD patients in the "southern group", then we ought to look for him in the Skara district or in the district marked Ma 4 Vä 2 (Malmbäck-Växjö). In this region we can also trace the forefathers of 6 GD parents.

The Skara district in the region of the "southern group" and the Skellefteå-Burträsk district in the region of the "Västerbotten group" have a common feature - *metalliferous deposits in the bedrock*.

In the Skellefteå-Burträsk area there are several sulphide ores located, containing among other elements copper, lead, zinc and arsenic. These ores are used as raw materials in the Rönnskär factories situated in the same district. Above these ores lie alun slates containing several heavy metals. Finally, in the uppermost layers, in soils and plants of strictly limited areas, there are anomalous high concentrations of metals, for example arsenic, lead, chromium and uranium.

As long as these heavy metals lie biologically inactive in ore bodies, they are harmless to man, but when they are mined and refined a genetical risk can occur.

In an article in *Environmental Health Perspectives* (3) it is reported that workers at the above-mentioned Rönnskär smeltery show a 10-fold increase in chromosomal aberrations in lymphocytes under mitosis compared with a normal material. The aberrations are thought to be an effect of arsenic, lead, selenium and other heavy metals in the factory smoke.

These signs of chromosomal damage, visibel under the microscope, might correspond to non-visible mutagenic damage, The Rönnskär smeltery has not been active for more than 50 years, and its effect on the incidence of recessive diseases, if there are any, can not be seen until 50 more years have elapsed.

On the contrary, the heavy metals in the surface soil have been available to human metabolism ever since the first colonizer came to the region.

The hypothesis of the author is that such heavy metals in the surface organic layers of the earth might be the mutagen agent responsible for the GD mutation both in the Skellefteå-Burträsk and in the Skara district of Sweden.

REFERENCES

1. Karl-Magnus Herrlin and Per-Olof Hillborg, Acta paediatrica, 137-154. March 1962.
2. R. Nyman and J. Lindsten, Advances in metabolic disorders, 7, 73-94. 1974.
3. G. Beckman, L. Beckman and I. Nordenson, Environmental health perspectives, 19, 145-146. 1977.

181

Copper in Sheep in Norway

Arne Frøslie

INTRODUCTION

Copper is widely used as a growth stimulant for fattening pigs. It is used at concentrations up to 250 mg/kg in the diet without severe risk of copper poisoning. Sheep, on the other hand, are very sensitive to excess of copper, and diet concentrations at only 1/10 of this level may prove toxic (Clarke & Clarke 1975, Hill 1977 a, b).

Housed sheep fed largely on concentrates are particularly sensitive to excess of copper in the diet, and chronic copper poisoning is well known under such feeding conditions. Sometimes this situation is accentuated by the addition of copper to the mixtures of concentrates.

Spontaneous chronic poisoning also, however, occurs in sheep under natural grazing conditions. In Australia such poisoning occurs under three sets of conditions (Hill 1977a,b, McCHowell 1977, Underwood 1977): (a) when the copper content of the pasture is abnormally high, (b) when the copper levels are normal but the molybdenum levels are low, and (c) in connection with the grazing of hepatotoxic plants.

In Norway chronic copper poisoning in sheep is well known. It occurs both on diets with high levels of concentrates, usually with copper added, and on natural pastures. The two kinds of poisoning seem to be equally important (Frøslie 1977).

The form of poisoning occurring in sheep under natural grazing conditions was described by Nordstoga (1962). This poisoning is mainly seen in the autumn, especially in sheep on mountain pastures, but also in the lowlands. The poisoning is well known in several inland districts in south-eastern and central Norway, and is also seen in the northern part of the country (Frøslie 1977).

Copper deficiency, on the other hand, has been reported from some coastal districts in Norway (Frøslie 1977). Copper deficiency in cattle also occurs in certain areas (Dynna & Havre 1963). In many countries copper deficiency in ruminants is a definite problem (Underwood 1977).

The aim of the present investigation was to describe the copper status of sheep in Norway.

MATERIALS AND METHODS

Liver samples from 582 adult sheep and 220 lambs were collected at different slaughterhouses in the autumn of 1974 and 1975. Origin of the samples is shown in Table 1. The lambs were selected from districts where chronic copper poisoning had occurred, and 119 of these animals came from one single herd. The samples were stored at -18°C until the analyses were done. Five-g samples were digested with sulphuric acid/nitric acid/perchloric acid, and the copper contents were determined by atomic absorption spectroscopy.

RESULTS AND DISCUSSION

The results of the analyses, which are presented in Table 1 and Figure 1, revealed a very large variation in the concentrations of liver copper in adult sheep. The ratio between the highest and the lowest value was higher than 400. Furthermore, there were wide variations between districts both in the mean values and the ranges.

In Akershus, Oppland, Hedmark, Buskerud, Trøndelag and Nordland the mean values were 2-3 times as high as the values from Vestlandet.

In the lambs there were also variations in copper levels, but to a lesser degree than in adult sheep. The ratio between the extreme values in the lambs was 85, and even among lambs from the single herd, there was a range of 34-340 μg Cu/g liver.

From the literature it is difficult to state definitive levels of normal copper concentrations in sheep liver. The following figures seem reasonable (Anon. 1973, Clarke & Clarke 1975, Underwood 1977):

Table 1. Copper concentrations in liver of adult sheep and lambs collected at slaughterhouses in Norway in the autumn of 1974 and 1975. The mean values (μg/g wet weight), ranges, and distribution below 10 μg/g and above 150 μg/g are given.

| | Numbers | Mean | Ranges | % of the samples | |
				< 10 μg/g	> 150 μg/g
Sheep					
Akershus/Oppland/					
Hedmark	72	204	19–820	0	54
Buskerud	132	181	7–830	1	52
Vestfold	20	83	7–250	10	25
Telemark	50	100	14–390	0	18
Agderfylkene	50	101	2–320	2	18
Rogaland	53	84	3–390	15	23
Vestlandet	50	54	5–230	6	2
Trøndelag	67	177	27–660	0	49
Nordland	48	151	3–670	4	38
Troms	40	91	22–220	0	18
All sheep	582	138	2–830	3	34
Lambs					
Akershus/Oppland	178	127	8–340	1	34
Buskerud	30	64	4–200	23	17
Trøndelag	12	106	38–150	0	0
All lambs	220	117	4–340	4	30

Upper marginal limit   150 μg Cu/g liver (wet weight)

Normal   about 50 μg Cu/g liver (wet weight)

Lower marginal limit   10 μg Cu/g liver (wet weight)

Levels lower than 3 μg Cu/g liver indicate copper deficiency. In the diagnostic work at our laboratory, levels of copper in the liver have always been higher than 150 μg Cu/g in connection with clinically or pathologically diagnosed copper poisoning.

In the two columns to the right in Table 1, percentages of the samples beyond the respective marginal levels are given. In those districts with high copper levels, 40-50 per cent of the

185

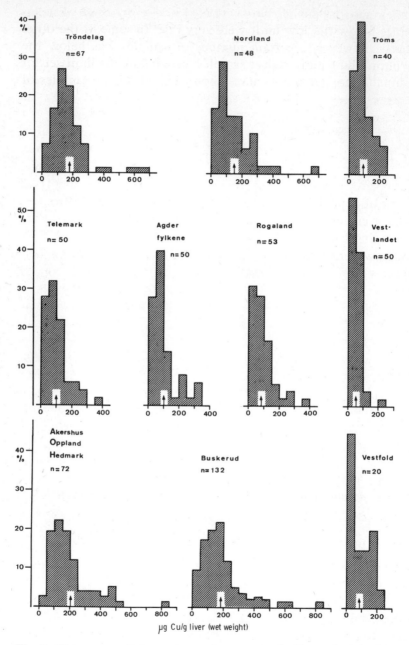

Fig. 1. Histograms of the content of copper in the liver of adult sheep collected at slaughterhouses in Norway in the autumn of 1974 and 1975.

samples showed higher levels than 150 µg. In these districts samples below the low limit were very rare. In some of the other districts, however, a certain number of samples was below the low limit, and totally 4 liver samples were below the limit set for presumable copper deficiency. About 1/3 of all the samples of adult sheep examined had values higher than 150 µg Cu/g

It may therefore be concluded that the supply of copper to sheep is sufficiently high almost throughout the country, and in wide areas there is a massive overloading. Copper supplementation is therefore necessary only in a few districts. The general supplementation of copper to sheep in Norway has increased the risk of copper poisoning and will be avoided in the future.

The occurrence of high copper loading in inland areas reflects the binding capacity of copper to the soil particles (Låg 1977). It is, however, difficult to state more precise relationships between geology and medicine in connection with chronic copper poisoning in sheep. The very great variation in copper levels in lambs from one single herd grazing together on the same natural pastures indicates that the aetiology of copper accumlation in sheep is rather complex. Other nutritional factors, such as molybdenum and sulphur, which are well-known interfering elements, most probably play important roles in the copper metabolism of sheep in our country too, but have not been sufficiently investigated in relation to sheep nutrition in Norway (Nordstoga & Havre 1971). Zinc may also be an interfering element in this connection (Dynna & Havre 1963). However, no relationship was found between copper, zinc, and molybdenum in the sheep liver (Frøslie & Norheim 1976).

There is no evidence that hepatotoxic plants interfere with spontaneous copper poisoning in sheep in Norway.

REFERENCES

Anon.: Tracing and treating mineral disorders in dairy cattle. Ed.: Committee on mineral nutrition. Centre for agricultural publishing and documentation, Wageningen 1973, 27-31.

Clarke, E.G.C., & M.L. Clarke: Veterinary toxicology. London 1975, 438 pp.

Dynna, O., & G.N. Havre: Interrelationship of zinc and copper in the nutrition of cattle. A complex zinc-copper deficiency. Acta vet. Scand., 1963, 4, 197-208.

Frøslie, A.: Kobberstatus hos sau i Norge. Norsk vet.-tidsskr., 1977, 89, 71-79.

Frøslie, A., & G. Norheim: The concentrations of molybdenum and zinc in liver in relation to copper accumulation in normal and copper poisoned sheep. Acta vet. Scand., 1976, 17, 307-315.

Hill, R.: Copper toxicity.I. Brit. vet. J., 1977a, 133, 219-224.

Hill, R.: Copper toxicity.II. Brit. vet. J., 1977b, 133, 365-373.

Låg, J.: Personal communication. 1977.

McC. Howell, J.: Chronic copper toxicity in sheep. Vet. Annual, 1977, 7, 70-73.

Nordstoga, K.: Undersøkelser over en særlig form for kopperforgiftning hos sau. (Investigations on a special kind of copper poisoning in sheep.) 9. Nordisk veterinærkongress, København 1962, 196-201.

Nordstoga, K., & G.N. Havre: The effect of copper dressing on the copper content of mountain pasture. Acta vet. Scand., 1971, 12, 122-124.

Underwood, E.J.: Trace elements in human and animal nutrition. 4th ed., New York 1977, 545 pp.

Trace Elements in Human Serum. Regional Distribution in Norway

Jon Jonsen, Kristen Helgeland, Eiliv Steinnes

Epidemiological studies have shown that the incidences of various human diseases exhibit regional differences (1,2). The reasons for these differences remain mainly obscure, but various factors, e.g. geochemistry, pollution, and food habits, have been considered (1). The exposure to metals has recently received considerable interest, and as geochemical surveys have been carried out in several countries, correlation of disease to such data has been sought (3-6). As various sources add to the intake of metals in humans, correlation with geochemical data might, however, be of uncertain value. We have therefore started on a project to measure the amount of different metals and other trace elements in blood serum from humans living in different communities, selected from areas with high and low incidence of multiple sclerosis, diabetes, coronary heart disease, and pernicious anemia.

Serum was obtained from 10 different communities, Lom, Vestre Slidre, Østre Slidre, Vang, Etnedal and Østre Toten in Oppland county and Gamvik, Porsanger, Kautokeino and Vadsø in Finnmark county. Except for Vadsø these are rural communities. The blood donors were of both sexes, and the majority was between 35 and 49 years old, with 10% being of the age from 20 to 34.

Blood was obtained by venipuncture, using the Venoject [R] vacuum sampling system. The blood was collected in tubes without any additives. After clotting and centrifugation, the serum fraction was transferred to a polystyrene tube (A/S Nunc, Denmark). The serum samples were sent by mail and frozen at −20°C upon receipt.

The serum samples were analysed for trace elements by atomic absorption spectrometry and neutron activation analysis.

189

ATOMIC ABSORPTION SPECTROMETRY

Zn and Cu were measured by aspiration of undiluted serum from a micro sampling cup into an air-acetylene flame, whereas Mn, Cr and Ni were measured by flameless technique. No pretreatment was carried out on the serum samples prior to the determination of Mn and Cr, whereas Ni was extracted with APCD-MIBK.

NEUTRON ACTIVATION ANALYSIS

Aliquots of 1 ml were irradiated for 2 days in the JEEP-II reactor at a thermal neutron flux of 1.5×10^{13} n cm^{-2} s^{-1}. After 5 days' delay the samples were decomposed with HNO_3/H_2SO_4 in the presence of carriers, and the elements of interest were separated by a radiochemical procedure involving a distillation (As, Se, Hg, Sb) and an anion exchange step (Zn, Fe). The radioactivity measurements were carried out by Ge(Li) γ-spectrometry. Chemical yields of the carriers were determined by re-irradiation.

RESULTS

Table 1 shows that the mean values for the serum content of copper and in particular zinc in the communities of Oppland exhibit only small variations. For zinc also a rather restricted range of the individual values is evident. In Finnmark a somewhat different picture emerges, with the same mean content for copper in the 4 communities investigated, whereas zinc varies from Gamvik with 1.2 μg/ml to Porsanger with 0.8 μg/ml as mean values.

For manganese similar values were found for the 3 rural communities Lom, Vestre Slidre, and Kautokeino, whereas in the urban area of Vadsø the mean serum content was lower by about 50%.

Chromium has only been measured in the 2 communities Vestre Slidre and Kautokeino, the latter showing a mean value of about two times that of Vestre Slidre.

The mean values for nickel showed rather small variations, with a high value of 1.4 ng/ml in Etnedal and a low value of 1.1 ng/ml. in Lom.

190

	Zn (µg/ml)			Cu (µg/ml)			Mn (ng/ml)			Cr (ng/ml)			Ni (ng/ml)		
	M	R	SD N	M	R	SD N	M	R	SD N	M	R	SD N	M	R	SD N
Opppland															
Lom	1.1	0.8–1.7	0.1(199)	1.2	0.7–2.2	0.2(199)	1.6	1.0–2.8	0.4(46)				1.1	0.7–1.7	0.3(40)
Etnedal	1.0	0.6–1.5	0.1(199)	1.1	0.6–1.8	0.2(196)							1.4	0.4–3.6	0.9(39)
Vang	1.0	0.6–1.5	0.1(198)	1.2	0.7–2.2	0.2(195)							1.2	0.6–2.7	0.4(40)
Østre Slidre	1.0	0.6–1.5	0.1(200)	1.2	0.8–2.2	0.2(200)							1.3	0.5–2.9	0.5(40)
Vestre Slidre	1.0	0.8–1.5	0.1(200)	1.1	0.1–1.8	0.2(198)	1.7	1.0–3.4	0.4(49)	0.7	0.1–2.0	0.4(49)	1.3	0.6–3.3	0.4(40)
Østre Toten	1.0	0.8–1.7	0.1(200)	1.0	0.6–2.1	0.2(199)							1.3	1.0–2.3	0.3(40)
Finnmark															
Gamvik	1.2	0.6–2.9	0.4(200)	1.1	0.6–2.8	0.3(200)									
Porsanger	0.8	0.5–2.1	0.2(200)	1.1	0.6–2.8	0.3(200									
Kautokeino	1.1	0.7–1.8	0.2(199)	1.1	0.7–2.2	0.2(195)	1.9	1.2–3.6	0.4(50)	1.5	0.2–3.1	0.6(50)	1.3	0.7–2.6	0.4(40)
Vadsø	0.9	0.5–2.1	0.1(200)	1.1	0.6–2.4	0.2(200)	0.8	0.4–2.0	0.4(48)				1.3	0.7–3.1	0.5(40)

M = Mean, R = Range, SD = Standard deviation, N = Number of sera.

Table 1. Metal content of human sera from 10 communities in the counties of Oppland and Finnmark as measured by atomic absorption spectrometry.

When one compares the range and standard deviation obtained for the different metals, it is obvious that the serum content of copper and in particular zinc is more strictly controlled than manganese, chromium and nickel. This is illustrated in Figs. 1 and 2, which show the distribution of the individual values for Vestre Slidre.

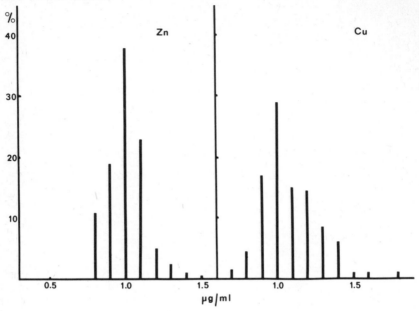

Fig. 1. Distribution of zinc and copper content of individual human sera obtained from Vestre Slidre in Oppland county. Measurements were carried out on 200 (Zn) and 198 (Cu) sera with atomic absorption spectrometry.

The data obtained so far for Se, Hg and Sb do not indicate any regional differences for these elements (Table 2). In the case of As, a somewhat higher mean value is evident in the case of Vadsø, as compared to the other areas investigated.

The reasons for the variations observed may vary, but factors such as age and sex, metal content of the drinking water, and geochemistry of the regions will be considered.

Any correlation to a prevalence of any of the mentioned diseases is also currently being elaborated.

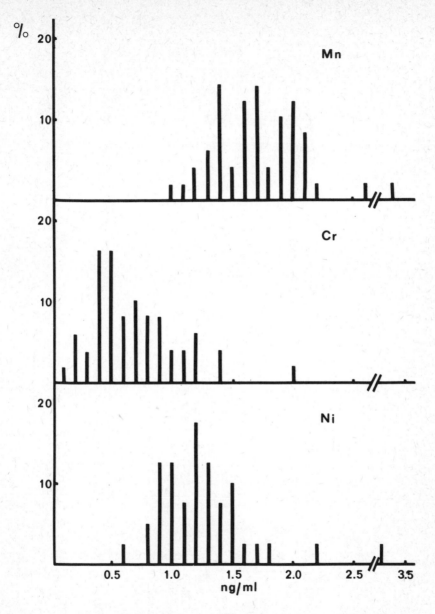

Fig. 2. Distribution of manganese, chromium and nickel content of individual sera obtained from Vestre slidre in Oppland county. Measurements were carried out on 49 (Mn), 49 (Cr) and 40(Ni) sera with flameless atomic absorption spectrometry.

Table 2. Trace elements in human sera from 8 communities in the counties of Oppland and Finnmark as measured by neutron activation analysis.

	N	As (ng/ml)			Hg (ng/ml)		Sb (ng/ml)		Se (ng/ml)			Zn (µg/ml)		
		M	R	SD	M	R	M	R	M	R	SD	M	R	SD
Oppland														
Lom	26	5.7	1.0–17	5.2	≤1.2	<0.5–2.3	≤1.0	<0.3–7.2	133	109–171	17	0.86	0.48–1.18	0.17
Etnedal	9	1.9	0.5–3.0	1.0	≤0.8	<0.5–1.7	≤0.5	<0.3–1.2	136	116–157	17	0.90	0.80–1.00	0.07
Vang	10	2.9	1.0–4.6	1.3	≤1.0	<0.5–1.6	≤0.6	<0.3–2.1	141	110–168	19	0.84	0.72–1.07	0.13
Østre Slidre	30	3.8	0.3–15	3.9	≤1.0	<0.3–2.4	≤0.6	<0.3–1.9	132	90–165	17	0.83	0.56–1.40	0.15
Vestre Slidre	10	3.7	1.1–7.7	2.3	≤1.4	<1 –3.2	≤0.9	<0.3–3.4	136	117–157	13	1.00	0.78–1.89	0.32
Østre Toten	10	2.3	0.3–5.8	1.8	≤1.5	<0.4–2.9	0.7	0.4–1.6	116	89–139	13	1.01	0.53–2.00	0.49
Finnmark														
Kautokeino	30	4.1	0.6–20	4.7	≤1.3	<0.5–2.3	≤0.4	<0.3–1.1	149	133–199	17	0.89	0.72–1.16	0.11
Vadsø	48	13.0	0.8–36	10.1	≤1.6	<0.5–4.7	≤0.6	<0.3–5.7	132	99–178	19	0.81	0.53–1.10	0.14

M = Mean, R = Range, SD = Standard deviation, N = Number of sera.

REFERENCES

1. World Health Organization (1972) Health hazards of the human environment, Geneva, Switzerland.
2. US Department of Health, Education, and Welfare (1975) Atlas of cancer mortality for US counties 1950 - 1969, Washington D.C. (Publication No. (NIH) 75-780).
3. Tourtelot, H.A. (1978) Geochemical surveys in the United States in relation to health: Report at The Royal Society, London, August 1978, Environmental Geochemistry and Health.
4. Thornton, I. (1978) Geochemistry and health in the United Kingdom: Ibid.
5. Shamberger, R.J. and Willis, C.E. (1971) Selenium distribution and human cancer mortality, CRC Crit. Rev. Clin. Lab. Sci. 2:211.
6. Marjanen, H. (1969) Possible causal relationship between the easily soluble amount of manganese on arable mineral soil and susceptibility to cancer in Finland. Ann. Agric. Fin. 8:326.

Introductory Geomedical Investigations in Norway

R. T. Ottesen

Fellow of the Norwegian Cancer Society
– Landsforeningen mot Kreft

INTRODUCTION

With funds from the Norwegian Cancer Society, the Geological Survey of Norway, in cooperation with the Agricultural University of Norway and the University of Oslo, has started a project to investigate possible correlations between geochemical and medical data in Norway.

This paper deals with some preliminary results concerning the chemical composition of stream sediments in central southern Norway (Fig. 1) and the correlation to the prevalence of multiple sclerosis within the same area.

METHODS

Details of the techniques employed in the stream sediment sampling and of the analytical procedures have been described by Bølviken and Sinding-Larsen (1972) and Bølviken et al. (1976). The samples in this study were collected in populated areas from streams of magnitude 1-3 (Sharp and Jones 1975). The survey area was covered by 1333 sample sites, the average density being 1 sample per 4 km^2. The samples were analysed for V, Mn, Fe, Co, Ni, Cu, Zn and Pb.

The prevalence data for multiple sclerosis were provided by Westlund (1970 and personal communication).

The relationship between 'municipality average' metal concentration (median values) and the prevalence values for multiple sclerosis has been examined by means of scatter diagrams and correlation coefficients.

197

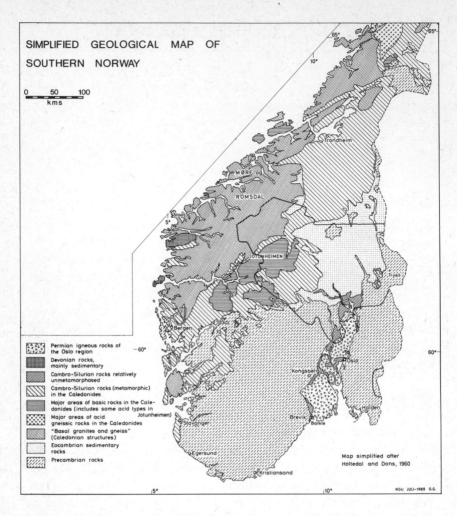

Fig. 1. Simplified geological map of southern Norway indicating the survey ares.

RESULTS

The concentration of heavy metals is approximately lognormally distributed so that their frequency distributions form more or less straight lines when plotted on logarithmic probability paper, and consequently, the median concentration for each chemical element in the individual municipalities has been used for comparisons with the prevalence data for multiple sclerosis (Tab. 1).

198

Table 1. Median concentrations of heavy metals in stream sediments and prevalence data for multiple sclerosis in 35 municipalities in central southern Norway.

Municipality	No. of sample sites	V ppm	Mn ppm	Fe %	Co ppm	Ni ppm	Cu ppm	Zn ppm	Pb ppm	*Prevalence MS/1000	Population (1960)
Lesja	39	26	180	0.87	7	10	10	20	6	1.03	2 925
Skjåk	30	21	195	0.75	6	9	7	23	6	1.74	2 868
Dovre	25	37	210	1.42	10	24	13	28	7	1.67	3 003
Lom	26	30	225	1.43	10	12	16	35	9	4.16	2 884
Vågå	28	37	225	1.43	11	21	17	30	8	1.73	4 044
Sel	34	42	300	1.68	13	17	21	40	9	0.95	5 291
Fron	47	28	525	1.80	12	18	16	53	12	0.51	9 727
Vang-Opp	126	47	560	1.80	12	13	17	49	16	1.53	1 962
V. Slidre	72	28	1075	2.80	17	20	20	70	18	2.44	2 464
Ø. Slidre	13	42	2100	3.45	20	30	18	88	17	1.43	2 789
Ringebu	31	18	490	1.95	12	16	13	61	18	2.50	5 589
Gausdal	50	42	525	1.80	12	24	12	49	12	1.06	6 600
Øyer	20	24	810	2.10	12	18	13	70	18	1.28	3 907
N. Aurdal	40	26	1000	2.40	16	26	18	88	18	0.53	5 649
Etnedal	35	23	1150	1.68	12	20	11	81	20	2.59	1 933
S. Aurdal	39	26	490	1.30	9	10	7	42	14	1.97	4 063
N. Land	40	24	1150	1.67	12	18	10	75	16	0.77	6 484
Lillehammer	20	26	1000	1.55	12	16	9	66	12	0.97	18 624
Gjøvik	41	26	600	1.22	9	11	8	46	12	0.82	23 159
S. Land	25	26	370	1.23	8	9	6	40	13	1.06	6 624
V. Toten	17	37	600	1.95	13	23	9	61	12	1.16	10 335
Gran	28	37	600	1.55	11	13	10	56	14	1.26	11 884
Jevnaker	9	37	525	1.55	10	14	11	46	17	1.36	4 535
Lunner	8	60	525	2.60	18	49	13	130	21	2.16	5 086
Ringsaker	48	21	1225	1.55	11	18	8	61	21	0.47	27 483
Vang-Hed	10	18	1800	1.22	8	17	5	66	21	0.26	7 703
Løten	15	20	525	1.15	7	12	6	49	9	0.16	6 270
Elverum	44	18	810	1.30	8	7	4	40	11	0.75	13 297
Åmot	54	9	300	0.70	4	5	2	12	7	0.90	5 542
Trysil	129	18	525	1.00	6	5	4	39	12	0.73	8 199
Stor-Elvdal	56	11	420	0.70	5	5	4	36	8	0.23	4 406
Rendal	48	10	320	0.61	4	2	3	17	7	0.54	3 721
Engerdal	37	5	455	0.66	5	6	4	47	10	1.66	1 807
Rømskog	13	16	100	0.49	4	1	2	14	9	6.93	721
Marker	64	21	100	0.75	7	3	4	24	10	0.57	3 530
Total survey Area	1333	24	560	1.55	10	12	9	45	12	1.02	235 108

* Prevalence data for multiple sclerosis are quoted from K. Westlund (pers. com.).

All the elements produce similar geographical distributions, of which the Ni pattern is a typical example (Fig. 2). The stream sediments from the northern Gudbrandsdal (Skjåk and Lesja), the Østerdalene (Elverum, Trysil, Stor-Elvdal, Rendalen and Engerdal), and the two municipalities in Østfold (Rømskog and Marker) have low metal content compared with the Valdres district (Ø. and V. Slidre, Etnedal and N. Aurdal).

Another type of distribution pattern is found in central Oppland. In this region the high and low values are distributed more or less uniformly throughout the area, and clustering is not so distinct as in the previously mentioned districts.

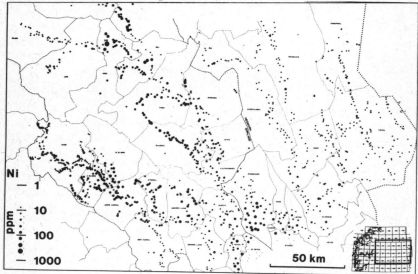

Fig. 2. HNO₃-soluble Ni in the minus 180 micron fraction of sediments from stream of magnitude 1 − 3 (Sharp and Jones 1975) in central southern Norway.

A large, high-risk area for multiple sclerosis is found along the main mountain range of southern Norway, with various extensions towards the lowlands and the sea (Westlund 1970).

The main conclusion of this study so far is that there seems to be no correlation between the prevalence of multiple sclerosis in municipalities in central southern Norway and the corresponding concentration of HNO_3-soluble V, Mn, Fe, Co, Ni, Cu, Zn and Pb in the minus 180 micron fraction of inorganic stream sediments (Tab. 2).

200

Table 2. Correlation coefficients between the prevalence of multiple sclerosis in 35 municipalities in central southern Norway (Westlund, personal communication) and the corresponding concentration of HNO_3-soluble V, Mn, Fe, Co, Ni, Cu, Zn and Pb in the minus 180 micron fraction of inorganic stream sediments.

Variables entered	Correlation coefficient (r)
MS – Pb	– 0.028
MS – Zn	– 0.098
MS – Ni	– 0.026
MS – Co	– 0.056
MS – Cu	0.059
MS – Mn	– 0.237
MS – Fe	– 0.027
MS – V	0.049

COMMENTS ON THE GEOCHEMICAL METHODS

By virtue of their origin, stream sediments represent composite samples of soils and rocks found in the area upstream from the sample point. The stream bed as a chemical system is, via sorption processes, in dynamic equilibrium with the chemical constituents of the stream water (Steele and Wagner 1975). The stream sediments are, therefore, a convenient sample medium for representation of the drainage areas. Sediments are often preferred instead of water samples, because the metal content of water fluctuates in relation to climatic and other secondary factors. Difficulties are also involved in transportation and analyses of water samples (Webb 1971).

Previously, geochemical stream sediment surveys have been used mainly in mineral exploration where the purpose is to locate anomalous high metal concentrations. In geomedical investigations, however, the purpose is to find regional variations in the background geochemistry. For problems of this type it is important to be aware of the limitations inherent in geochemical stream sediment surveys. An essential question in this connection is to what extent the metal status of the natural environment is reflected by the metal content of the stream sediments.

This problem should be further investigated in order to make full use of stream sediments as a sample medium for geomedical investigations.

201

ACKNOWLEDGEMENTS

The financial support from the Norwegian Cancer Society is gratefully accepted. The following persons have helped during various phases of this work: B. Bølviken, J. Ekremsæther, H. Hovdan, J. Jonsen, M. Kvåle-Jensen, J. Låg, L. Ottesen, K. Reitan, M. Reitan, T. Volden and K. Westlund.

REFERENCES

Armour-Brown, A., & I. Nichol, 1979. Regional geochemical reconnaissance and the location of metallogenic provinces. Econ. Geol., 65, 312-330.

Armstrong, R.W. 1964. Environmental factors involved in studying the relationship between soil elements and disease. Amer. J. publ. Hlth, 54, 1536-1544.

Aston, S.R., I. Thornton, J.S. Webb, J.B. Purves, & B.L. Milford. 1974. Stream sediment composition: an aid to water quality assessment. Water, air and soil pollution, 3, 321-325.

Anotria, V., & C.Y. Chork. 1976. A study of the application of regression analysis for trace element data from stream sediment in New Brunswick, J. geochem. explor., 6, 211-232.

Barr, D.A., & H.E. Hawkes. 1963. Seasonal variations in copper content of stream sediments in British Columbia. Trans Am. Inst. Min. Eng., 226, 342-346.

Berry, R.W., & P. Jørgensen. 1971. Grain size, mineralogy and chemistry of a quick-clay sample from the Ullensaker Slide, Norway. Eng. Geol., 5, 73-84.

Bjørlykke, A., B. Bølviken, P. Eidsvig, & S. Svinndal. 1973. Exploration for disseminated lead in southern Norway. In: Jones (ed.), Prospecting in areas of glacial terrain. London IMM, 111-126.

Brinck, J.W., & A. Hofmann. 1964. The distribution of beryllium in the Oslo region, Norway, a geochemical, stream sediment study. Econ. Geol., 59., 59, 79-96.

Brundin, N.H., & B. Nairis. 1972. Alternative sample types in regional geochemical prospecting. J. geochem. explor., 1, 7-46.

Bølviken, B. 1967. Recent geochemical prospecting in Norway. In: Kvalheim (Ed.), Geochemical prospecting in Fennoscandia, 225-253.

Bølviken, B. 1972. Geokjemisk kartlegging av metallinnhold i bekkesedimenter. Symposium om tungmetall-forurensning, Hurdalsjøen hotell 14. - 16. februar 1972.

Bølviken, B., & R. Sinding-Larsen. 1972. Total error and other criteria in the interpretation of stream-sediment data. In Jones (ed.), Geochemical exploration 1972, London IMM, 285-195.

Bølviken, B., J.R. Krog, & G. Næss. 1976. Sampling technique for stream sediments. J. geochem. explor., 5, 382-383.

Bølviken, B., & J. Låg. 1976. Naturlig tungmetallforgiftning av jordsmonn. Naturen, 1, 11-17.

Bølviken, B., & P.E. Paus. 1976. Snertingdal, II: extraction of lead from various size fractions of stream sediments. J. geochem. explor., 5, 331-335.

Callahan, J. 1976. A geochemical survey of stream sediments in Watanga county, North Carolina. J. geochem. explor., 6, 61-73.

Campbell, A.M.G., G. Herdan, W.F.T. Tatlow, & E.G. Whittle. 1950. Lead in relation to disseminated sclerosis. Brain, 73, 52-71.

Cannon, H.L., & H.C. Hopps. 1970. Geochemical environment in relation to health and disease. Geol. Soc. Am. Spec. Paper, 140.

Chao, T.T., & B. Anderson. 1974. The scavenging of silver by manganese and iron oxides in stream sediments collected from two drainage areas of Colorado. Chem. Geology, 14, 159-166.

Chatupa, J., & K. Fletcher. 1972. Application of regression analysis to the study of background variations in trace metal content of stream sediments. Econ. Geol., 67, 978-980.

Chork, C.Y. 1977. Seasonal, sampling and analytical cariations in stream sediment surveys. J. geochem. explor., 7, 31-47.

Connor, J.J., & H.T. Shacklette. 1975. Background geochemistry of some rocks, soil plants and vegetables in the conterminous United States. U.S. Geol. Surv. Prof. Paper 574 - F.

Ellis, A.J., J.S. Tooms, J.S. Webb, & J.V. Bicknell. 1967. Application of solution experiments in geochemical prospecting. Trans. IMM Sect. B, 76, 25-39.

Englund, J.O., & P. Jørgensen. 1973. A chemical classification system for argillaceous sediments and factors affecting their composition. Geol. Fören. Förh., 95, 87-97.

Evensen, E. 1974. Kornfordelingens innflytelse på blyinnholdet i bekkesedimenter. Unpubl. NGU report.

Fletcher, K. 1970. Some applications of background correction to trace metal analysis of geochemical samples by atomic absortion spectrophotometry. Econ. Geol., 65, 588-591.

Follestad, B.A. 1974. Kart over "naturlige" forurensninger. Tekn. ukeblad, 25/1974.

Fortescue, J.A.C. 1971. A preliminary study of relationships between patterns on topographic, geological, land use and geochemical maps of the area around St. Catharines, Ontario, Canada. In: Hemphill (ed.), Trace substances in environmental health, V, 497-514. University of Missouri.

Foster, J.R. 1971. The reduction of matrix effects in atomic absorption analysis and the efficiency of selected extractions on rockforming minerals. CIM Spec., 11, 554-560.

Freedman, J. 1975. Trace element geochemistry in health and disease. Geol. Soc. Am. Spec. Paper 155.

Förstner, U., & G. Muller. 1974. Schwermetalle in Flussen und Seen, Berlin.

Garrett, R.G., & I. Nichol. 1967. Regional geochemical reconnaissance in eastern Sierra Leone. Trans. IMM Sect. B, 76, 97-112.

Gibbs, R.J. 1973. Mechanisms of trace metal transport in rivers. Science, 180, 71-73.

Gibbs, R.J. 1976. Transport phases of transition metals in the Amazon and Yubeon Rivers. Geol. Soc. Am. Bull., 88, 829-843.

Goldschmidt, V.M. 1954. Geochemistry. Oxford.

Gorham, E. 1961. Factors influencing supply of major ions to inland waters with special reference to the atmosphere. Geol. Soc. Am. Bull., 72, 795-840.

Govett, G.J.S. 1961. Seasonal variation in the copper concentration in drainage systems in Northern Rhodesia. Trans. IMM, 70, 177-189.

Govett, G.J.S., & R.E. Whitehead. 1973. Errors in atomic absorption spectrophometric determinations of Pb, Zn, Ni and Co in geologic materials. J. geochem. explor., 2, 121-131.

Grout, F.F. 1925. Relation of texture and composition of clays. Bull, Geol. Soc. Am., 36, 393-416.

Hawkes, H.E., 7 H. Bloom. 1956. Heavy metals in stream sediment used as exploration guides. Mining engineering. November 1956, 1121-1127.

Hawkes, H.E., & J.S. Webb. 1962. Geochemistry in mineral exploration. New York.

Hjulstrom, F. 1935. Studies of the morphological activity of rivers as illustrated by the river Fyris. Geol. Inst. Univ. Uppsala, Bull., 25, 221-527.

Holtedahl, O. 1960. Geology of Norway. Norges geol. unders. 208.

Holtedahl, O., & J.A. Dons. 1960. (map) In: Holtedahl, O. (ed.), Geology of Norway. Norges geol. unders. 208.

Hopps, H.C. 1971. Geography, geochemistry and disease. In: Hemphill (ed.), Trace substances in environmental health, V, 475-484. University of Missouri.

Howarth, R.J., & P.L. Lowenstein. 1971. Sampling variability of stream sediments in broad-scale regional geochemical reconnaissance. Trans. IMM Sec. B, 80, 363-372.

Howarth, R.J., & M. Thompson. 1976. Duplicate analysis in geochemical practice. Part II. Examination of proposed method and examples of its use. Analyst, 101, 669-709.

204

Ingamells, C.O., J.C. Engels, & P. Switzer. 1972. Effect of laboratory sampling error in geochemistry and geochronology. 24th Int. Geol. Congr., Sect. 10, 405-415.

Jenne, E.A. 1968. Controls on Mn, Fe, Co, Ni, Cu and Zn concentrations in soils and waters: the significant role of hydrous Mn and Fe oxides. Advanc. Chem., 73, 337-388.

Jørgensen, P. 1977. Some properties of Norwegian tills. Boreas, 6, 149-158.

Koch, G.S., & R.F. Link. 1970-1971. Statistical analysis of geological data, 1-II. New York.

Krauskopf, K.B. 1967. Introduction to geochemistry. New York.

Kurtzke, J.F. 1966. An evaluation of the geographic distribution of multiple sclerosis. Acta neurol. scand., 42, 91-117.

Kurtzke, J.F. 1974. Further features of the Fennoscandian focus of multiple sclerosis. Acta neurol. scand., 50, 478-502.

Kurtzke, J.F. 1975. A reassessment of the distribution of multiple sclerosis. Part 1. Acta neurol. scand., 51, 110-136.

Kurtzke, J.F. 1975. A reassessment of the distribution of multiple sclerosis. Part 2. Acta neurol. scand., 51, 137-157.

Lahermo, P. 1971. On chemical denudation caused by ground water in central finnish Lapland. Bull. Geol. Soc. Finl., 43, 233-246.

Leake, R.C., & R.T. Smith. 1975. Comparison of stream sediment sampling methods in parts of Great Britain. Vancouver IGES, 579-594.

Levinson, A.A. 1974. Introduction to exploration geochemistry. Calgary.

Låg, J. 1972. Soil science and geomedicine. Acta agric. scand., 22, 150-152.

Låg. J., & B. Bølviken. 1974. Some naturally heavy-metal poisoned areas of interest in prospecting, soil chemistry and geomedicine. Norges geol. unders., 304, 73-96.

Låg, J., & E. Steinnes. 1978. Regional distribution of selenium and arsenic in humus layers of Norwegian forest soils. Geoderma, 20, 3-14.

Låg, J. 1970. Registreringen av hovedtyper av jordsmonn i skogene, i Norge. In: Taksering av Norges skoger, Landskogstakseringen 50 år, 1919-1969. Oslo: 143-149.

McNeal, J.M. 1974. Trace element mode of occurrence in stream sediments. Geol. Soc. of Am., Abstracts, 6, 866.

Merefield, J.R. 1974. Major and trace element anomalies in stream sediments of the Teign Valley Orefield. J. geochem. explor., 3, 151-166.

Miesch, A.T. 1967. Theory of error in geochemical data. U.S. Geol. Surv. Prof. Paper 574 - A.

Morisawa, M. 1968. Streams, their dynamics and morphology. New York.

Nichol, I., & A. Bjørklund. 1973. Glacial geology as a key to geochemical exploration in areas of glacial overburden with particular reference to Canad. J. geochem. explor., 2, 133-170.

205

Nordseth, K. 1974. Sedimenttransport i norske vassdrag. NVE-Statskraftverkene. Februar 1974.

Oftedal, S.I. 1965. Multiple sclerosis in Vestfold country. Acta neurol. scand., 41, 7-59.

Plant, J. 1971. Orientation studies on streamsediment sampling for a regional geochemical survey in northern-Scotland. Trans. IMM Sect. B, 80, 324-345.

Plant, J., K. Jeffrey, E. Gill, & C. Fage. 1975. The determination of accuracy and precision in geochemical exploration data. J. geochem. explor., 4, 467-486.

Presthus, J. 1966. Multiple sclerosis in Møre og Romsdal county, Norway. Acta neurol. scand., 42, 12-18.

Rankama, K., & T.G. Sahama. 1950. Geochemistry, Chicago.

Refsum, S. 1960. Multipel sklerose. Medisinsk årbok, 1959-60, 264-275. Oslo.

Refsum, S., & J. Presthus. 1966. Multipel sklerose. Medicinsk årbog, IV, 286-297. København.

Rinne, U.K., M. Panelius, E. Kivalo, E. Hokkanen, & J. Palo. 1966. Distribution of multiple sclerosis in Finland with some special reference to some geological factors. Acta neurol. scand., 42, 385-399.

Rose, A.W., E.C. Dahlberg, & M.L. Keith. 1970. A multiple regression technique for adjusting background values in stream sediment geochemistry. Econ. Geol., 65, 156-165.

Rose, A.W., N.H. Suhr. 1971. Major element content as a means of allowing for background variation in stream sediment geochemical exploration. CIM Spec. Vol., 11, 587-593.

Rosenqvist, I. 1975. Chemical investigations of tills in the Numedal. Geol. fören. Förh., 97, 284-286.

Rove, O.N. 1926. Undersøkelser over norske lerer, VI. Petrografiske undersøkelser. Statens Råstoffkomite, publikasjon 23.

Salmi, M. 1963. On the relations between geology and multiple sclerosis. Acta geographic., 17, 3-13.

Schock, W.W., & J.R. Steidtmann. 1976. Relations between stream sediment and source-rock mineralogy, Piney Creek Basin, Wyoming. Sedimentary Geology, 16, 281-297.

Sharp, W.E., & T.L. Jones. 1975. A topologically optimum prospecting plan for streams. Vancouver IGES, 227-235.

Smith, D.C. 1976. Grong: the correlation of altitude and the tree line with lead in stream sediments. J. geochem. explor., 5, 227-231.

Steele, K.F., & G.H. Wagner. 1975. Trace metal relationships in bottom sediments of a fresh water stream – the Buffalo River, Arkansas. J. sedimentary petrology, 45, 310-319.

206

Thornton, I., & J.S. Webb. 1973. Environmental geochemistry: Some recent studies in the United Kingdom. In: Hemphill (ed.), Trace substances in environmental health, VII, 89-98. University of Missouri.

Underwood, E. 1971. Trace elements in human and animal nutrition. New York.

Ward, F.N., H.M. Nakagawa, T.F. Haims, & G.H. VanSickle. 1969. Atomic absortion methods of analysis useful in geochemical exploration. U.S. Geol. Surv. Bull., 1289.

Warren, H.V. 1962. Does geology hold a key to better health? Mining engineering, July 1962, 41-45.

Warren, H.V. 1967. Possible correlations between geology and some disease pattern. Ann. N.Y. Acad. Sci., 136, 657-710.

Webb, J.S. 1971. Regional geochemical reconnaissance in medical geography. Geol. Soc. Am. Memoir, 123, 31-41.

Webb, J.S., I. Nichol, & I. Thornton. 1968. The broadening scope of regional geochemical reconnaissance. XXIII Int. Geol. Cong., 6, 131-147.

Wedepohl, K.H. 1969-1972. Handbook of geochemistry. Vol I-IV. Berlin.

Westlund, K. 1970. Distribution and mortality time trend of multiple sclerosis and some other diseases in Norway. Acta neurol. scand., 46, 385–409.

Whitney, P.R. 1973. Variation of heavy metal content with particle size in stream sediments. Geol. Soc. Am. Abstracts, 5, 238.

Whitney, P.R. 1975. Relationship of manganese-iron oxides and associated heavy metals to grain size in stream sediments. J. geochem. explor., 4, 251-263.

Wikström, J. 1975. Studies on the clustering of multiple sclerosis in Finland. Department of Neurology, University of Helsinki.

Woodsworth, G.J. 1971. A geochemical drainage survey and its implications for metallogenesis, Central Coast Mountains, British Columbia. Econ. Geol., 66, 1104-1120.

The Effect of Some Heavy Metals on Oats in Pot Experiments with Three Different Soil Types

Asbjørn Sorteberg

An account is given of two pot experiments, one of which (F. 73) has included all combinations of 5 heavy metals (cadmium, cobalt, lead, mercury, and nickel), 3 rates of each metal (0, 50, and 250 mg/pot a 5 litres), 2 rates of lime, and 3 types of soil (clay soil, peat soil, and sandy soil), The experiment has run for 4 years (1973-1976). The second experiment (F. 74) has run for three years (1974-1976) and included the same soil types and lime rates, but only cadmium and mercury of the metals, at the rates of 0, 0.5, and 5 mg/pot. The crop grown has in all the years been oats, and two parallels have been used for each treatment. A third parallel without crop has been used for soil sampling only.

Fifty mg metal, or less, per pot had little or no effect on the crop yield, while 250 mg of all metals, except lead, had a distinct yield-reducing effect (Tab. 1). Mercury induced a near total crop failure in the sandy soil series (Series VI) in the first and partly also in the second year, whereas the yield was normal from the third year of the experimental period. The peat soil series (Series V) and the clay soil series (Series I) showed distinct yield reduction after application of mercury in the first year. Cadmium, nickel and cobalt generally reduced the yield in all soil series throughout the entire experimental period, particularly after light liming. Yield reduction by nickel has been all but eliminated after heavy liming. Heavy liming has also greatly counteracted the yield reduction by cobalt. Yield figures with cadmium present a less distinct picture, because the yield was greatly reduced by *manganese deficiency* after heavy liming.

209

Table 1. F.73. Oats, relative yield of dry matter (grain + straw) for 250 mg metal per 5 litre pot.

Heavy metals	Soil series	1973 L.l.	1973 H.l.	1974 L.l.	1974 H.l.	1975 L.l.	1975 H.l.	1976 L.l.	1976 H.l.	Means L.l.	Means H.l.
	I	96	89	84	94	92	96	66	78	84	89
Cd	V	84	83	97	88	82	30	73	104	84	76
	VI	97	102	91	97	97	69	78	62	91	83
	I	41	100	51	103	55	98	78	97	56	99
Ni	V	27	86	48	103	88	98	81	115	61	101
	VI	37	107	58	101	77	82	81	98	63	97
	I	78	95	114	120	109	102	101	99	101	104
Hg	V	79	70	116	106	101	103	94	95	98	94
	VI	6	6	0	114	134	95	98	93	59	77
	I	99	98	115	104	98	100	97	92	102	99
Pb	V	101	101	113	101	103	106	91	123	102	108
	VI	103	104	98	102	93	90	98	96	98	98
	I	65	77	70	100	64	95	86	94	71	91
Co	V	82	87	93	92	78	100	68	94	80	93
	VI	85	105	90	106	72	101	69	96	79	102

Without metal = 100. L.l. = Light liming. H.l. = Heavy liming. Series I = Clay soil. Series V = Peat soil. Series VI = Sandy soil.

The reduction in yield due to nickel at light liming was considerable for the first two years, but the negative effect decreased during the last years of the experimental period, i.e. the yield increased in relation to the control. This did not apply to cadmium and cobalt.

	Rel. yield, means for soil series			
	1973	1974	1975	1976
Nickel	35	52	73	80
Cadmium	92	91	90	72
Cobalt	77	84	71	74

210

High amount of cadmium has delayed the ripening by up to one week at both rates of lime. High amount of nickel at light liming led to the development of elongated white lines and white spots on older leaves, and delayed the ripening by up to three weeks. High amount of cobalt at both lime rates in series V led to interveinal chlorosis that may suggest iron deficiency.

Table 2. F. 73. 1973–76. Heavy metals in oats, mg/kg dry matter.

Heavy metals	Year	Soil series	Grain Light liming 0	50	250	Grain Heavy liming 0	50	250	Straw Light liming 0	50	250	Straw Heavy liming 0	50	250
Cd	M.1.–3.	I	0.09	5.35	9.91	0.07	2.28	5.42	0.20	9.38	31.3	0.17	2.50	9.13
		V	0.07	8.29	16.1	0.03	4.85	8.38	0.15	30.3	93.3	0.15	17.1	43.0
		VI	0.20	6.26	13.6	0.11	2.36	6.64	0.22	11.8	54.6	0.19	3.36	13.1
	1.		0.11	7.91	18.1	0.7	3.89	8.97	0.18	25.3	94.0	0.14	13.9	42.0
	2.		0.19	7.41	12.5	0.11	3.36	6.65	0.29	17.4	51.6	0.23	5.23	14.3
	3.		0.06	4.57	8.95	0.03	2.24	4.83	0.11	8.76	33.7	0.15	3.76	9.00
	4.		0.15	2.76	6.00	0.12	2.26	4.90						
Ni	M.1.–4.	I	3.28	20.1	59.2	0.98	3.43	10.9	0.66	2.72	23.6	0.78	0.64	1.24
		V	0.97	62.8	105	0.25	29.5	72.1	0.67	18.8	68.5	0.54	6.60	29.1
		VI	1.26	24.2	88.6	0.71	8.15	32.5	0.80	4.57	61.0	0.80*	0.65*	7.47
	1.		1.44	42.1	113	0.73	19.1	44.8	0.22	11.9	80.2	<0.20**	5.49**	18.0
	2.		2.62	41.9	91.5	1.00	16.3	46.7	1.34	10.4	60.7	1.55	2.92	14.5
	3.		1.65	34.2	73.9	0.29	12.2	35.2	0.33	7.64	40.1	<0.20	1.63	10.1
	4.		1.63	24.5	57.9	0.54	7.16	27.4	0.77	4.86	23.2	0.70	2.08	7.48
Pb	M.1.–4.	I	0.21	0.33	0.39	0.34	0.31	0.28	2.09	2.07	2.80	2.10	2.34	2.53
		V	0.30	0.52	2.57	0.26	0.33	0.58	1.29	4.25	14.5	1.51	2.00	5.01
		VI	0.27	0.30	0.51	0.23	0.34	0.43	1.71	2.14	2.87	1.76	2.01	2.22
	1.		0.23	0.37	0.87	0.30	0.27	0.50	1.51	2.67	6.52	1.72	2.15	4.46
	2.		0.37	0.68	1.77	0.46	0.63	0.82	2.47	3.87	7.83	2.22	2.59	3.59
	3.		0.18	0.29	1.22	0.17	0.12	0.14	1.58	2.53	6.82	1.95	1.67	2.33
	4.		0.24	0.36	0.76	0.17	0.28	0.26	1.23	2.24	5.68	1.26	2.05	2.63
Co	M.1.–4.	I	<0.6	1.68	7.12	<0.6	0.42	1.39	0.46	5.47	23.7	0.50	0.92	2.82
		V	<0.6	3.89	16.7	<0.3	1.87	7.71	0.32	16.7	70.7	0.37	8.74	31.6
		VI	<0.6	1.43	9.38	<0.6	-0.58	1.82	0.52*	6.17	33.0	0.50*	1.86	6.41
	1.		<0.10**	3.49	17.3	<0.1**	1.71	5.77	0.14**	18.4	79.3	<0.1**	8.09	26.5
	2.		<0.6	2.36	10.3	<0.6	0.97	3.06	0.63	9.36	42.2	0.84	3.77	12.6
	3.		0.1	1.83	8.69	<0.1	0.50	2.43	0.26	5.84	24.7	<0.2	1.70	7.77
	4.		0.28	1.65	7.97	<0.3	0.64	3.31	0.57	4.09	20.3	0.59	1.79	7.52

* 1. year omitted   ** Series VI omitted.

The contents of cadmium, nickel, lead and cobalt in the crop are presented in Tab. 2, and for mercury in Tab. 3. Apart from lead, the content increased strongly after application of 50 and 250 mg metal per pot. The contents of cadmium, nickel and cobalt increased substantially more at light than at heavy liming. The contents of cadmium, nickel, lead and cobalt rose substantially more in series V than in the remaining two series, and least in series I. The exceptionally high content of mercury in series VI at the highest mercury application is partly a function of the low yield.

Table 3. F.73. Hg in dry matter of oats, μg/kg.

		Grain						Straw					
		Light liming			Heavy liming			Light liming			Heavy liming		
Soil						Added Hg, mg per pot (5 l)							
series	Year	0	50	250	0	50	250	0	50	250	0	50	250
I.	1.	5	*	257	8	32	53	32	95	1263	83	132	1000
	4.	10	9	9	10	10	15	22	25	26	20	32	21
V	1.	45	182	631	43	271	310	114	737	8540	58	705	8421
	4.	<4	9	10	<4	5	9	14	56	30	18	39	28
VI	1.	<20	151	**	25	140	**	106	3436	99000	26	1712	39000
	4.	<4	8	9	<4	11	<5	21	26	22	24	20	32

* Analysis error   ** No yield

For all metals except nickel, the content was much higher in straw than in grain, while the opposite occurred for nickel.

The content of cadmium, nickel and cobalt shows a falling trend throughout the experimental period. The mercury content proves nearly normal in the fourth year, even after heavy application of the metal.

In F. 74 even as small an amount as 0.5 mg/pot of cadmium led to a strong increase in cadmium in grain as well as in straw. Mercury at the 0.5 and 5 mg level only led to a slight increase in straw, mainly in series V. The effect on grain proved difficult to establish.

At harvesting time soil samples were taken from the pots without plants for chemical analyses of all metals added. The method of Egner, Riehm and Domingo (AL-solution) was used for the extraction. Tab. 4 gives the amounts of metals extracted from soil in per cent of the amounts applied to the soil of cadmium, nickel and cobalt.

The amounts of AL-soluble metals decrease for all metals from the first to the third or the fourth year. In the case of cadmium, this is roughly equal to the increased amount of metal removed with the crop. For nickel, and particularly for cobalt, the reduction in metal exceeds the increased removal.

High rate of lime resulted in lower levels of AL-soluble heavy metals (Table 4). The difference was particularly marked for cobalt (23%) and nickel (18%), as compared to only 4% for cadmium (mean values for soil series and years).

Table 4. F.73. Cd, Ni and Co in soil samples extracted by AL-solution, per cent of added. Means of the 2 rates of metal and the 3 soil series.

Metal	Liming	Year 1.	2.	3.	4.	Means
Cd	Light	53	54	44	47	50
	Heavy	46	51	41	44	46
	Means of liming	50	53	43	46	48
	Light minus heavy	7	3	3	3	4
Ni	Light	53	54	52	46	51
	Heavy	37	36	33	27	33
	Means of liming	45	45	43	37	42
	Light minus heavy	16	18	19	19	18
Co	Light	56	50	45	45	49
	Heavy	34	26	23	22	26
	Means of liming	45	38	34	34	38
	Light minus heavy	22	24	22	23	23

The figures in Table 4 conceal substantial variations. The variations between soil series are notable. Expressed as mean values of years and rates of lime these amounts of cadmium and nickel have been recovered, in per cent of the amounts applied:

Soil series	I	V	VI
Cd	36	52	54
Ni	24	58	44

In the case of cobalt, the effect of heavy liming on the AL-soluble fraction has been dependent on the soil type. The effect of lime has been much less for the peat soil (Series V) than for the two mineral soils:

	Light liming	Heavy liming
Soil series I	30	9
Soil series V	65	53
Soil series VI	52	16

Roughly 10% has been extracted as AL-soluble lead after both lime rates.

The amounts of mercury extracted by the AL-method amounted to only 2-3% of the amounts applied. Mercury was also extracted using 2 M HCl. The figures, in per cent, are given below:

	50 mg Hg		250 mg Hg	
	1973	1976	1973	1976
Soil series I	92	92	69	90
Soil series V	81	108	91	76
Soil series VI	115	49	36	18

Even in the first year, some of the mercury has probably disappeared from the sandy soil, or been insoluble at the highest application rate.

REFERENCES

Andersson, A., and K.O. Nilsson. 1977. Influence of lime and soil pH on Cd availability to plants. Ambio, 5, 198-200.

Andersson, A., och K.O. Nilsson, 1975. Effekter på tungmetallhalterna i mark och växt ved tillförsel av rötslam som växtnäringskälla och jordförbättringsmedel. Rapport nr. 96 från avdelningen för växtnäringslära, Lantbrukshögskolan, Uppsala.

Coppenet, M., E. More, L. Le Corre et M. Le Mao. 1972. Variations de la teneur en cobalt des ray-grass; etude de techniques d'enrichissement. Ann.agron., 23(2), 165-196.

Cox, W.J., and D.W. Rains. 1972. Effect of lime on lead uptake by five plant species. J. of environ. qual., 1, No. 2, 167-169.

Egner, H., H. Riehm and W.R. Domingo. 1960. Untersuchungen über die chemische Bodenanalyse als Grundlage fur die Beurteilung des Nährstoffzustandes der Böden. II. Chemische Extractionsmethoden zur Phosphor- und Kaliumbestimmung. Kungl. Lantbr. högsk. Ann., 26, 199-215.

Ivai, I., T. Hara, and Y. Sonoda. 1975. Factors affecting cadmium uptake by the corn plant. Soil Sci. Plant Nutr., 21(1), 37-46.

Jansson, S.L. 1975. Kadmium i växtnäringsbalansen. Seminar om tungmetaller, sirkulasjon i jordbruket, 24-31. NJF Seksjon I.

John, M.K. 1976. Interrelationships between plant cadmium and uptake of some other elements from culture solutions by oats and lettuce. Environ. Pollut., (11)2, 85-95.

John, M.K., and C. Van Laerhoven. 1972. Lead uptake by lettuce and oats as affected by lime, nitrogen, and sources of lead. J. of environ. qual., 1, No. 2, 169-171.

Linnman, L., A. Andersson, K.O. Nilsson, B. Lind, T. Kjellström and L. Friberg. 1973. Cadmium uptake by wheat from sewage sludge used as a plant nutrient source. Arch. environ. Health, 27, 45-47.

Miller, J.E., J.J. Hassett, and D.E. Koeppe. 1976. Uptake of cadmium by soybeans as influenced by soil cation exchange capacity, pH, and available phosphorus. J. environ. qual., 5, No. 2, 157-160.

Sorteberg, A. 1974. The effect of some heavy metals on oats in a pot experiment with three different soil types. J. Sci. Agric. Soc. Finland, 3, 277-288.

Williams, C.H., and D.J. David. 1976. The accumulation in soil of cadmium residues from phosphate fertilizers and their effect on the cadmium content of plants. Soil Sci., 121, No. 1, 86-93.

Regional Distribution of Arsenic, Selenium and Antimony in Human Layers of Norwegian Soils

E. Steinnes

There is evidence that some human diseases may be connected with regional differences in soil chemistry. For a long time it was generally assumed that the chemical composition of soils could be explained on the basis of local geology. More recently it has become clear that airborne supply both from natural and anthropogenic processes may also make a very significant contribution to the surface layer of soils. Thus, the importance of atmospheric input to the chemical composition of soils in Norway has been clearly demonstrated for several elements associated with the marine environment (Låg, 1968; Låg & Steinnes, 1972, 1974, 1976, 1978).

There is also some indication that the composition of surface soils may be influenced by long-range transport of pollutants. Analyses of the moss Hylocomium Splendens (Ruhling & Tyler, 1973; Steinnes, 1977) indicate that the airborne supply of some elements is as much as a factor of ten higher in the southernmost part of Norway than in some of the more northerly parts of the country. A study of ombrogenous peat (Hvatum, 1971) showed a higher accumulation of lead in the surface layer in southern than in northern parts of Norway. In a recent investigation of selenium and arsenic in humus samples from the counties of Nord-Trøndelag, Oppland, and Buskerud, relatively high concentrations of both elements were found in the southern districts of Eastern Norway (Låg & Steinnes, 1978).

In order to facilitate further studies of the geographical distribution of trace elements in Norwegian surface soils, including the significance of long-distance air pollution, about 500 humus samples regularly distributed throughout the country were collected during the summer of 1977. This material is at present under investigation with respect to several elements potentially associated with air pollution. The first results available are for arsenic, selenium and antimony, which have it in common that they form volatile compounds that can be released to the atmosphere during the burning of coal and other human activities. All three elements are known to be highly enriched in aerosols relative to major elements in the earth's crust (e.g. Peirson et al., 1974; Duce et al., 1975).

The analytical determinations were carried out by neutron activation analysis. Since the analyses are relatively time-consuming, only about 100 samples were selected for this investigation. The samples were chosen in a way that would reveal any concentration differences between the southermost districts and more northerly areas, as well as possible differences bestween coastal and inland districts at the same latitude.

About 10 samples were taken from each of the following regions:

1. Southermost Norway, coastal districts
2. Western Norway, coastal districts
3. Interior parts of (1) and (2)
4. Northern valleys of Eastern Norway
5. Møre/Trønderlag, coastal districts
6. Møre/Trønderlag, interior
7. Nordland, coastal districts
8. Nordland, interior
9. Troms/Finnmark, coastal districts
10. Troms/Finnmark, interior

The location of the regions and sampling points are shown in Fig. 1.

The results are listed in Table 1 as arithmetic mean values for each region. Relative figures based on the values of region no. 1 are also given in the table. The results of As and Sb show a remarkably similar trend. The As/Sb ratio is quite constant at a value of about 4 in the whole area studied. The highest concentrations are found in the southernmost parts of Norway, but high values are also observed in coastal districts of Western Norway. Considerably lower levels are found in the more interior

218

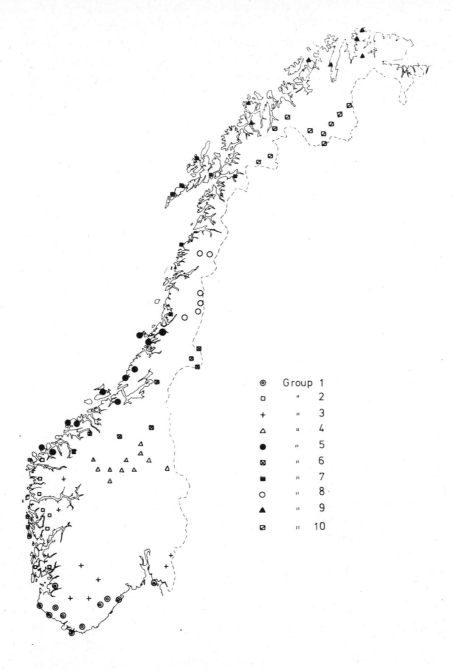

Fig. 1. Map of Norway showing the sample locations.

Group 1
" 2
" 3
" 4
" 5
" 6
" 7
" 8
" 9
" 10

Table 1. Concentration of arsenic, selenium, and antimony in the humus layer of soils from different regions in Norway.

Region no.*	As		Se		Sb	
	ppm	Rela-tive figure	ppm	Rela-tive figure	ppm	Rela-tive figure
1	8.80	1.00	2.32	1.00	2.20	1.00
2	5.53	0.63	1.81	0.78	1.09	0.50
3	2.74	0.31	0.80	0.34	0.84	0.38
4	0.98	0.11	0.36	0.16	0.22	0.10
5	1.56	0.18	1.64	0.71	0.33	0.15
6	0.80	0.09	0.63	0.27	0.25	0.11
7	1.75	0.20	1.47	0.63	0.41	0.19
8	1.43	0.16	0.53	0.23	0.31	0.14
9	0.75	0.09	1.15	0.50	0.23	0.10
10	0.69	0.08	0.31	0.13	0.17	0.08

* Se text for explanation

parts of these regions. Also further north the coastal regions show higher concentrations than their interior counterparts. A difference of more than a factor of 10 is evident between the coastal districts of southernmost Norway and the interior districts of the northernmost part of the country. The observed results cannot be explained by regional differences in geology.

The results for As and Sb in soils show a very similar trend to that previously indicated by moss analysis (Steinnes, 1977). The observed results may thus to a large extent be explained by airborne supply, mainly from sources out of Norway. Local pollution sources may be assumed to contribute only a minor part.

Selenium shows a distinctly different distribution to that of As and Sb. Previous work (Låg & Steinnes, 1974, 1978) showed a decreasing concentration of Se in soils with increasing distance from the sea, indicating airborne supply of the element from the marine environment. This trend is supported by the present work. The selenium distribution observed here can be explained as consisting mainly of two parts: a pollution-derived component with a distribution similar to that of As and Sb, and a natural component with a possible marine origin.

It may also be mentioned that preliminary data for lead in the whole material collected, determined by atomic absorption spectrometry, indicate a geographical distribution very similar to that of As and Sb. For cadmium a somewhat similar distribution seems to be evident. For these elements too it seems difficult to explain the observed distribution without assuming atmospheric input from external sources.

It thus appears that a considerable accumulation of some potentially toxic elements, associated with long-distance transport of pollutants, takes place in the humus layer of soils in certain regions of Norway. The possible influence of this process on human health and the natural biological system is not known, but possible harmful effects cannot be excluded. Since the air-borne supply of these elements is likely to continue in the years to come, an increased effort as regards studies in this area is desirable.

REFERENCES

Duce, R.A., G.L. Hoffman, & W.A. Zoller. 1974. Atmospheric trace metals at remote northern and southern hemisphere sites: Pollution or natural? Science, 187, 59-61.

Hvatum, O.Ø. 1971. Sterk blyopphopning i overflatesjiktet i myrjord. Spesielt fremtredende i Sør-Norge. Teknisk ukeblad, 118, 40.

Låg, J. 1968. Relationships between the chemical compositions of the precipitation and the contents of exchangeable ions in the humus layer of natural soils. Acta agric. scand., 18, 148-152.

Låg, J., & E. Steinnes. 1972. Distribution of chlorine, bromine and iodine in Norwegian forest soils studied by neutron activation analysis. In: Isotopes and radiation in soil-plant relationships including forestry. International Atomic Energy Agency, Vienna, pp. 383-395.

Låg, J., & E. Steinnes. 1974. Soil selenium in relation to precipitation. Ambio, 3, 237-238.

Låg, J., & E. Steinnes. 1976. Regional distribution of halogens in Norwegian forest soils. Geoderma, 16, 317-325.

Låg, J., & E. Steinnes. 1978. Regional distribution of selenium and arsenic in humus layers of Norwegian forest soils. Geoderma, 20, 3-14.

Peirson, D.H., P.A. Cawse, & R.S. Cambray. 1974. Chemical uniformity of airborne particulate material, and a maritime effect. Nature, 251, 675-679.

Ruhling, Å., & G. Tyler. 1973. Heavy metal deposition in Scandinavia. Water, air and soil pollution, 2, 445-455.

Steinnes, E. 1977. Atmospheric deposition of trace elements in Norway studied by means of moss analysis. Report KR-154. Institutt for atomenergi, Kjeller, Norway.

Geomedical Aspects in Present and Future Research

Symposium

arranged by The Norwegian Academy of Science and Letters in collaboration with The Academies of Sciences of Denmark, Finland, Iceland, and Sweden, and sponsored by The Nordic Culture Fund and The Norwegian Cancer Society.

Oslo, 22 – 23 May 1978

Participants

DENMARK:

Overlæge dr. Johannes Clemmesen, Pathologiafdelingen – Finseninstitutet, København.

Lic. agro. Gunnar Gissel Nielsen, Risø nasjonallaboratorium, afd. landbrug, Roskilde.

Dyrlæge Mogens G. Simesen, Institut for intern medicin, Den kgl. Veterinær- og Landbohøjskole, København.

ENGLAND:

Dr. Iain Thornton, Applied Geochemistry Research Group, Department of Geology, Royal School of Mines, Imperial College of Science and Technology, London.

FINLAND:

Professor dr. Joakim Donner, Institutionen för geologi och paleontologi, Helsingfors Universitet, Helsingfors.

Inspektör mag. Helvi Marjanen, Lantbrukets Forskningscentral – Byrån för lokala fältförsök, Helsingfors.

Dr. Esko Saari, Kemira Oy, Oulu Research Laboratory, Oulu (Uleåborg).

ICELAND:

Professor Ólafur Bjarnason, Rannsóknastofa Háskólans í Meinafrædi, Háskóli Íslands, Reykjavík.

Dr. Sturla Fridriksson, Rannsóknastofnun Landbúnadarins, Reykjavík.

. Overdyrlege Páll A. Pálsson, Tilraunastöd Háskólans í Meinafrædi, Háskóli Íslands, Reykjavík.

SWEDEN:

Leg. läk. Britt Ahlrot-Westerlund, Danderyd.

Förste statsgeolog Herman Brundin, Sveriges Geologiska Undersökning, Stockholm.

Byråchef Allan Danielsson, Sveriges Geologiska Undersökning, Stockholm.

Förste statsgeolog John Ek, Sveriges Geologiska Undersökning, Stockholm.

Chefapotekare Jan Emberg, Danderyds sjukhus, Danderyd.

Barnläk. med.lic. Per-Olof Hillborg, Sollentuna.

Professor Göran Jönsson, Veterinärinrättningen i Skara - Försöksgården, Skara.

Docent Bo Pehrson, Veterinärinrättningen i Skara - Försöksgården, Skara.

Fil. mag. Gunnar Schalin, Esselte Map Service, Stockholm.

Chefapotekare Kicks de Vahl, Danderyds sjukhus, Danderyd.

U.S.A.:

Ernst L. Wynder, M.D., President of the American Health Foundation, New York (N.Y.).

NORWAY:

Forsøksleder dr. Harald N. Astrup, Institutt for husdyrnæring og fôringslære, Norges landbrukshøgskole, Ås.

Professor dr. Johannes Barstad, Statens institutt for folkehelse, Oslo.

Professor dr. Kåre Berg, Institutt for medisinsk genetikk, Universitetet i Oslo, Oslo.

Dosent dr. Harald Bergseth, Institutt for jordbunnslære, Norges landbrukshøgskole, Ås.

Overlege Kjell Bjartveit, Statens skjermbildefotografering, Oslo.

Professor dr. Tor Bjerkedal, Hygienisk institutt, Universitetet i Oslo, Oslo.

Dr. Kari Blegen, Norges Teknisk-Naturvitenskapelige Forskningsråd, Oslo.

Førstegeokjemiker Bjørn Bølviken, Norges geologiske undersøkelse, Trondheim.

Dr. ing. Hans C. Christensen, Norges Teknisk-Naturvitenskapelige Forskningsråd, Oslo.

Dosent dr. Finn Devik, Institutt for patologi, Universitetet i Oslo — Rikshospitalet, Oslo.

Konsulent Torstein Engelskjøn, Norges almenvitenskapelige forskningsråds utredningsinstitutt, Oslo.

Avdelingsveterinær Arne Frøslie, Veterinærinstituttet, Oslo.

Spesiallege dr. Tore Godal, Det Norske Radiumhospital, Oslo.

Direktør dr. Knut S. Heier, Norges geologiske undersøkelse, Trondheim.

Prosektor Kristen Helgeland, Odontologisk institutt for mikrobiologi, Universitetet i Oslo, Oslo.

Professor dr. Eigil Hesstvedt, Institutt for geofysikk, Universitetet i Oslo.

Cand. real Øystein Hov, Institutt for geofysikk, Universitetet i Oslo, Oslo.

Professor dr. Harald J. Hvidsten, Institutt for fjørfe og pelsdyr, Norges landbrukshøgskole, Ås.

Professor dr. Herman Høst, Det Norske Radiumhospital, Oslo.

Forskningsstipendiat dr. Ivar S. A. Isaksen, Institutt for geofysikk, Universitetet i Oslo, Oslo.

Professor dr. Olav Hilmar Iversen, Institutt for patologi, Universitetet i Oslo — Rikshospitalet, Oslo.

Professor dr. Jon Jonsen, Odontologisk institutt for mikrobiologi, Universitetet i Oslo, Oslo.

Cand. real. Hans Kristiansen, Norsk institutt for vannforskning (NIVA), postboks 333 — Blindern, Oslo 3.

Cand. med. vet. Rolf Bjerke Larsen, Instituttet for biokjemi, Norges veterinærhøgskole, Oslo.

225

Spesiallege Per G. Lund-Larsen, Statens skjermbildefotografering, Oslo.

Professor dr. Jul Låg, Institutt for jordbunnslære, Norges landbrukshøgskole, Ås.

Dr. Knut Magnus, Kreftregisteret, Institutt for epidemiologisk forskning, Det Norske Radiumhospital, Oslo.

Redaktør Mauritz S. Mortensen, Norges almenvitenskapelige forskningsråd, Oslo.

Siv. agr. Gunvor Nersten, Institutt for jordbunnslære, Norges landbrukshøgskole, Ås.

Professor dr. Henrich Neumann, Mineralogisk-geologisk museum, Universitetet i Oslo, Oslo.

Førsteamanuensis Gunnar Norheim, Veterinærinstituttet, Oslo.

Stipendiat Rolf Tore Ottesen, Norges geologiske undersøkelse, Trondheim.

Professor dr. Alexis C. Pappas, Kjemisk institutt, Universitetet i Oslo, Oslo.

Overlege Einar Pedersen, Kreftregisteret, Det Norske Radiumhospital, Oslo.

Professor dr. Alexander Pihl, Norsk Hydros Institutt for Kreftforskning, Det Norske Radiumhospital, Oslo.

Professor dr. Erik Poppe, Det Norske Radiumhospital, Oslo.

Professor dr. Sigvald Refsum, Rikshospitalets nevrologiske avdeling, Universitetet i Oslo, Oslo.

Professor dr. Olav Sandvik, Veterinærinstituttet, Oslo.

Professor dr. Arne Semb-Johansson, Zoologisk institutt, Universitetet i Oslo, Oslo.

Professor Asbjørn Sorteberg, Institutt for jordkultur, Norges landbrukshøgskole, Ås.

Dr. Eiliv Steinnes, Institutt for atomenergi, Kjeller.

Amanuensis Karl Tungesvik, Institutt for jordbunnslære, Norges landbrukshøgskole, Ås.

Professor dr. Knut Westlund, Institutt for samfunnsmedisin, Universitetet i Tromsø, Tromsø.